Earth's Healing Touch: Min(
Finding Inner Peace in the

Jakub Nowak

Copyright © [2023]

Author: Jakub Nowak

Title: Earth's Healing Touch: Mindful Practices for Finding Inner Peace in the Natural World

This book is a product of [Publisher's Jakub Nowak]

ISBN:

TABLE OF CONTENTS

Chapter 1: The Power of Nature Meditation

Understanding Nature Meditation

Nature has a profound ability to heal and bring us inner peace. In today's fast-paced and technology-driven world, many of us long for a connection with the tranquility and beauty of the natural world. Nature meditation is a powerful practice that allows us to tap into the restorative energies of the Earth and find solace amidst the chaos of everyday life.

Nature meditation is a form of mindfulness practice that involves immersing ourselves in the sights, sounds, smells, and sensations of the natural environment. It is about being fully present and engaged with the world around us, opening ourselves up to its infinite wisdom and healing powers. Whether it's a walk in the woods, sitting by the ocean, or simply gazing at a sunset, nature meditation allows us to find peace within ourselves by connecting with the peace of nature.

The practice of nature meditation is accessible to everyone, regardless of age, background, or spiritual beliefs. It requires no special equipment or training, just an open mind and a willingness to slow down and appreciate the wonders of the natural world. By taking the time to observe and connect with nature, we can cultivate a deep sense of gratitude, awe, and reverence for life.

One of the key benefits of nature meditation is its ability to reduce stress and anxiety. When we immerse ourselves in nature, our bodies naturally relax, and our minds become more calm and focused. The rhythmic sounds of waves crashing, the gentle rustling of leaves, or the chirping of birds can lull us into a state of deep relaxation and tranquility. As we let go of our worries and concerns, we can experience a profound sense of inner peace and harmony.

Nature meditation also allows us to develop a deeper connection with the Earth and all its living beings. We begin to recognize that we are not separate from nature but an integral part of the intricate web of life. This realization fosters a sense of interconnectedness, compassion, and respect for all living creatures, leading to a greater sense of purpose and meaning in our lives.

In conclusion, nature meditation is a powerful practice that can bring us inner peace and healing. It is a way to reconnect with the peace of nature and find solace in its beauty and wisdom. By immersing ourselves in the natural world, we can reduce stress, cultivate gratitude, and develop a deeper sense of connection with all living beings. So, take a moment to step outside, breathe in the fresh air, and allow the healing touch of the Earth to restore your mind, body, and spirit.

Defining nature meditation

In our fast-paced, technology-driven world, finding inner peace can often feel like an impossible task. We are constantly bombarded with distractions and demands, leaving us feeling overwhelmed and disconnected from ourselves and the natural world around us. However, there is a path to rediscovering inner peace – nature meditation.

Nature meditation is a practice that involves immersing oneself in the beauty and serenity of the natural world. It is a mindful practice that allows us to quiet our minds, let go of stress and worries, and reconnect with the peace and tranquility that nature offers.

Unlike traditional forms of meditation that are often practiced indoors, nature meditation encourages us to step outside and engage with the living world. It invites us to become fully present and aware of our surroundings – the sights, sounds, and smells of the natural environment. Whether we choose to meditate in a lush forest, beside a babbling brook, or on a sandy beach, nature provides the perfect backdrop for deepening our connection to ourselves and finding inner peace.

When we engage in nature meditation, we become attuned to the rhythms of the earth. We may notice the gentle sway of the trees, the rhythm of our breath matching the ebb and flow of the ocean waves, or the symphony of birdsong filling the air. As we immerse ourselves in these natural rhythms, our own internal rhythm begins to align, allowing us to experience a profound sense of calm and peace.

Nature meditation also offers us the opportunity to cultivate gratitude and appreciation for the beauty and abundance of the natural world. As we observe the intricate patterns of a flower, the delicate dance of a butterfly, or the majesty of a towering mountain, we cannot help but feel a sense of awe and wonder. This connection with nature nourishes our souls, reminding us of our place in the grand tapestry of life.

In the subchapter "Defining Nature Meditation" of the book "Earth's Healing Touch: Mindful Practices for Finding Inner Peace in the Natural World," readers of all walks of life are introduced to the transformative power of nature meditation. Whether you are seeking solace, peace of mind, or a deeper connection with the natural world, this practice can bring you the inner peace you desire. By embracing the practice of nature meditation, you can embark on a journey of self-discovery, finding solace and tranquility amidst the chaos of everyday life.

Exploring the benefits of nature meditation

In today's fast-paced and technology-driven world, finding inner peace and tranquility has become more important than ever. As human beings, we often find solace in connecting with nature, and one powerful way to do so is through the practice of nature meditation. This subchapter aims to delve into the immense benefits that nature meditation can bring into our lives, helping us find inner peace and harmony.

Nature meditation is a practice that involves immersing oneself in the natural world and using it as a focal point for mindfulness and meditation. It encourages us to slow down, breathe deeply, and fully engage with the environment around us. By doing so, we can tap into the healing power of nature and experience its many benefits.

One of the key advantages of nature meditation is its ability to reduce stress and anxiety. As we connect with the peacefulness and serenity of nature, our minds naturally calm down, and our stress levels decrease. The gentle sounds of a babbling brook, the rustling of leaves in the wind, or the chirping of birds become a soothing symphony that helps us relax and let go of our worries.

Moreover, nature meditation can also enhance our overall well-being and mental clarity. Being in nature allows us to disconnect from the constant noise and distractions of modern life, allowing our minds to find clarity and focus. Studies have shown that spending time in nature can improve our cognitive function, memory, and creativity, enabling us to think more clearly and make better decisions.

Furthermore, nature meditation helps us develop a deeper sense of gratitude and connection with the natural world. As we observe the intricate beauty and harmony of nature, we cannot help but feel a deep appreciation for the earth's wonders. This connection to nature can foster a sense of belonging and purpose, reminding us of our interconnectedness with all living beings.

Ultimately, nature meditation offers a path to finding inner peace and balance. By immersing ourselves in the peace of nature, we can cultivate a greater sense of calmness, joy, and contentment in our lives. It is an accessible practice that can be enjoyed by anyone, regardless of age or physical ability.

So, whether you find solace in a nearby park, a scenic mountain trail, or a quiet garden, take the time to explore the benefits of nature meditation. Allow yourself to be fully present in the natural world, embrace its healing touch, and discover the profound impact it can have on your overall well-being.

How nature meditation differs from traditional meditation practices

In the quest for inner peace and tranquility, meditation has long been a trusted practice. However, there is a lesser-known form of meditation that taps into the healing power of nature. Nature meditation, as the name suggests, is a unique practice that combines the principles of traditional meditation with the awe-inspiring energy of the natural world. In this subchapter, we will explore how nature meditation differs from traditional meditation practices and how it can bring about a profound sense of peace and connection to those who seek solace in the beauty of nature.

Unlike traditional meditation, which often involves sitting in a quiet room and focusing on the breath or a specific object, nature meditation encourages individuals to immerse themselves in the natural environment. Whether it is a lush forest, a serene beach, or a blooming garden, the goal of nature meditation is to connect with the Earth's healing touch and find inner peace through the wonders of the natural world.

One key difference between nature meditation and traditional meditation lies in the sensory experience. While traditional meditation often encourages practitioners to close their eyes and turn their focus inward, nature meditation invites individuals to open their senses to the sights, sounds, smells, and textures of the natural environment. By doing so, practitioners can fully embrace the present moment and experience a deep sense of connection with the world around them.

Furthermore, nature meditation emphasizes the interconnectedness of all living beings. It encourages individuals to recognize their place within the grand tapestry of nature and to cultivate a sense of gratitude and reverence for the Earth. This interconnectedness can be a powerful source of peace, as it reminds us that we are not separate from nature but rather an integral part of it.

Nature meditation also offers the opportunity for physical movement and exploration. Unlike traditional meditation, which is often practiced in a stationary position, nature meditation encourages individuals to engage in gentle walking, stretching, or even yoga amidst the natural surroundings. This movement not only helps to ground the practitioner but also deepens the connection between mind, body, and the natural world.

In conclusion, nature meditation is a unique and powerful practice that differs from traditional meditation in several ways. By immersing ourselves in the beauty of nature, opening our senses, embracing interconnectedness, and engaging in gentle movement, we can tap into the Earth's healing touch and find inner peace in ways that traditional meditation alone may not offer. So, whether you are seeking solace, connection, or a deeper appreciation for the wonders of the natural world, nature meditation is a pathway to finding inner peace amidst the peace of nature.

Connecting with the Natural Environment

In today's fast-paced, technology-driven world, it's easy to feel disconnected from the natural environment. We spend most of our time indoors, glued to screens, and surrounded by artificial lights and sounds. However, deep down, we all have a primal need to connect with nature and find peace within its embrace. In this subchapter, we will explore the profound benefits of connecting with the natural environment and offer mindful practices to help you find inner peace in the world around you.

Nature has an incredible healing touch that can bring us a sense of calm, serenity, and a renewed perspective on life. Whether it's the soothing sound of waves crashing on the shore, the gentle rustling of leaves in the wind, or the vibrant colors of a sunset, immersing ourselves in the natural world can be a transformative experience. Research has shown that spending time outdoors can reduce stress, improve mental health, increase creativity, and enhance overall well-being.

To connect with the natural environment, start by carving out time in your day to spend outside. Take a walk in a nearby park or forest, sit by a lake or river, or simply spend a few minutes in your backyard. As you venture into nature, be fully present in the moment. Notice the details around you – the scent of flowers, the texture of tree bark, the songs of birds. Engage your senses and let the natural world awaken your inner peace.

Another way to deepen your connection with nature is through mindful practices. Try practicing mindfulness while hiking, taking photographs of natural landscapes, or even by practicing yoga outdoors. These activities can help you cultivate a sense of gratitude, awe, and appreciation for the beauty that surrounds us. As you engage with nature mindfully, you'll discover that the peace of nature becomes intertwined with your own inner peace.

Remember, connecting with the natural environment is not just about finding temporary solace but also about nurturing a long-lasting relationship with the world around us. It's about recognizing that we are an integral part of nature and that our well-being is deeply interconnected with the health of the planet. By connecting with the natural environment, we can find the peace we seek and become advocates for its preservation.

So, whether you live in a bustling city or a rural area, make a conscious effort to connect with the natural environment. Embrace its healing touch and allow its peace to seep into your soul. As you do, you'll find that the world around you transforms into a sanctuary of tranquility, and your inner peace becomes intertwined with the peace of nature itself.

Developing an appreciation for nature

Subchapter: Developing an Appreciation for Nature

Introduction:
In our fast-paced and technology-driven world, it is easy to overlook the beauty and tranquility that nature offers. However, reconnecting with the natural world can have a profound impact on our overall well-being. This subchapter aims to guide readers from all walks of life in developing a deeper appreciation for nature, fostering a sense of peace and harmony within themselves.

1. The Healing Power of Nature:
Nature has long been recognized as a source of healing and rejuvenation. From the soothing sound of waves crashing on a beach to the invigorating scent of fresh pine, nature has a unique ability to calm our minds and restore our spirits. By taking the time to immerse ourselves in the natural world, we can tap into this healing power and experience a profound sense of peace.

2. Mindful Observation:
Developing an appreciation for nature begins with mindful observation. By consciously engaging our senses, we can connect with the intricate details of the natural world. Take the time to notice the vibrant colors of a sunset, the delicate petals of a flower, or the gentle rustling of leaves in the wind. Through mindful observation, we can cultivate gratitude for the beauty that surrounds us.

3. Immersion in Nature:
To truly appreciate nature, we must immerse ourselves in it. Find opportunities to spend time in natural settings, whether it be a local

park, a nearby forest, or a peaceful garden. Disconnect from the constant noise and distractions of modern life, and allow yourself to fully experience the serenity of nature. Through this immersion, we can develop a profound sense of peace that transcends our daily worries and concerns.

4. Cultivating a Connection:
Nature is not separate from us; we are an integral part of it. Developing a deep connection with nature involves recognizing our interconnectedness with all living beings and the Earth itself. Engage in activities such as hiking, gardening, or simply sitting in silence, and reflect on the ways in which we are interconnected with the natural world. This realization can foster a sense of peace and oneness with nature.

Conclusion:
In a world that often feels chaotic and overwhelming, developing an appreciation for nature can provide a much-needed respite. By mindfully observing, immersing ourselves, and cultivating a connection with the natural world, we can tap into the peace and harmony that nature offers. Let us embrace the healing touch of the Earth and find inner peace through our appreciation for nature.

Cultivating a sense of wonder and awe

In a fast-paced and technology-driven world, it is easy to lose touch with the beauty and tranquility that nature offers. However, reconnecting with the natural world can have profound effects on our well-being, bringing us a sense of inner peace and harmony. Cultivating a sense of wonder and awe is the key to unlocking the healing power of nature and finding inner peace.

Nature has a way of captivating us with its sheer magnificence. From the majestic mountains to the delicate petals of a flower, every aspect of the natural world holds its own unique charm. By opening ourselves up to the wonders of nature, we can tap into a wellspring of peace and tranquility that is always available to us.

One of the ways to cultivate a sense of wonder and awe is to practice mindfulness in nature. When we step outside and immerse ourselves in the natural environment, we can become fully present and engage our senses. Observe the colors of the landscape, listen to the melodies of the birds, feel the gentle caress of the wind on your skin. By being fully present in the moment, we can awaken a deep appreciation for the beauty around us.

Another powerful way to cultivate wonder and awe is through exploration. Take the time to venture into different natural settings, whether it be hiking through a lush forest, strolling along a serene beach, or simply sitting in a city park. Each encounter with nature presents an opportunity to discover something new and awe-inspiring. Be curious, ask questions, and allow yourself to be amazed by the intricacies of the natural world.

The more we cultivate a sense of wonder and awe, the more we realize our interconnectedness with nature. We begin to understand that we are not separate from the natural world, but rather an integral part of it. This realization can foster a deep sense of peace within us, as we recognize our place in the grand tapestry of life.

So, whether you are a nature enthusiast or someone seeking inner peace, cultivating a sense of wonder and awe is a transformative practice. By immersing ourselves in the beauty of the natural world and embracing its mysteries, we can find solace, inspiration, and a profound sense of inner peace. Let us open our hearts and minds to the healing touch of the Earth and allow wonder and awe to guide us on a journey towards finding inner peace in the embrace of nature.

Deepening your connection with the natural world

In our fast-paced, technology-driven world, it is easy to become disconnected from the beauty and serenity of nature. However, reconnecting with the natural world can bring immense peace and healing to our lives. In this subchapter, we will explore mindful practices that can help you deepen your connection with the natural world and find inner peace.

Nature has a profound ability to calm our minds and nourish our souls. It is a sanctuary where we can escape the stresses and anxieties of daily life. By consciously immersing ourselves in nature, we can tap into its innate healing power. Whether it is a walk in the park, a hike in the mountains, or simply spending time in your backyard garden, make a conscious effort to connect with nature regularly.

One way to deepen your connection with the natural world is through mindfulness. By practicing mindfulness, you can fully engage with the present moment and experience nature with all your senses. As you walk through a forest, notice the sensation of the earth beneath your feet, the smell of the trees, the sound of the birds, and the warmth of the sunlight on your skin. Allow yourself to be fully present and let nature's beauty wash over you.

Another practice to deepen your connection with nature is gratitude. Take a moment each day to express gratitude for the natural world around you. Reflect on the abundance of life, the beauty of the changing seasons, and the intricate interconnectedness of all living beings. By cultivating gratitude, you will develop a deeper appreciation for the peace that nature brings.

In addition to mindfulness and gratitude, consider incorporating rituals into your connection with the natural world. Create meaningful rituals that honor the cycles of nature, such as planting a tree on Earth Day or performing a full moon ceremony. These rituals can serve as reminders of our deep connection to the Earth and can help us align our inner selves with the natural world.

Remember, deepening your connection with the natural world is a personal journey. Find what resonates with you and embrace it. Whether it is through mindfulness, gratitude, rituals, or a combination of practices, the important thing is to make a conscious effort to prioritize your connection with nature. As you deepen this connection, you will find that the peace of nature becomes an integral part of your daily life, bringing you inner peace, harmony, and a renewed sense of well-being.

Mindfulness in Nature

Nature has a profound ability to bring us a sense of peace and tranquility. In a world filled with constant noise and distractions, finding solace in the natural world can be a transformative experience. The subchapter "Mindfulness in Nature" delves into the practice of connecting with nature as a means to find inner peace. Whether you are an avid nature enthusiast or someone seeking serenity, this chapter offers mindful practices that can be easily incorporated into your daily life.

In today's fast-paced society, it is easy to become disconnected from the world around us. We find ourselves consumed by technology, deadlines, and the demands of modern living. However, by immersing ourselves in nature, we can tap into a deeper sense of calm and rejuvenation. Mindfulness in nature is about being fully present in the moment, embracing the beauty and wonder of our natural surroundings.

This subchapter explores various techniques that can enhance your connection with nature. It encourages you to slow down and engage your senses fully. From mindful walks in the woods to meditation by a serene lake, you will discover practical exercises that will help you cultivate a greater appreciation for the peace nature offers.

The chapter also explores the healing power of nature and its ability to restore our overall well-being. Studies have shown that spending time in nature can reduce stress, anxiety, and even boost our immune system. By incorporating mindfulness into our encounters with nature, we can amplify these benefits and experience a profound sense of inner peace.

Additionally, "Mindfulness in Nature" suggests ways to incorporate nature into your daily routine, even if you live in a bustling city. Whether it is tending to a small indoor garden or taking short breaks outside during the day, these simple practices can reconnect you with the peace nature provides.

"Earth's Healing Touch: Mindful Practices for Finding Inner Peace in the Natural World" invites everyone to embrace the peace of nature, regardless of their background or lifestyle. By incorporating mindfulness into our interactions with the natural world, we can discover a profound sense of peace, tranquility, and harmony within ourselves. So, whether you are a nature lover seeking a deeper connection or someone yearning for a reprieve from the chaos of daily life, this chapter offers valuable insights and practical techniques to help you harness the healing power of nature and find inner peace.

Embracing mindfulness as a foundation for nature meditation

In today's fast-paced and chaotic world, finding inner peace has become a priority for many individuals seeking solace and tranquility. The beauty and serenity of nature have long been recognized as a powerful source of peace and rejuvenation. In our book, "Earth's Healing Touch: Mindful Practices for Finding Inner Peace in the Natural World," we delve into the transformative power of nature meditation and the importance of embracing mindfulness as a foundation for this practice.

Mindfulness is the art of being fully present in the moment, with a non-judgmental awareness of our thoughts, feelings, and physical sensations. When applied to nature meditation, mindfulness allows us to deepen our connection with the natural world, enabling us to experience its healing touch on a profound level.

Nature offers us a sanctuary from the stresses and demands of modern life. When we immerse ourselves in its wonders, we can let go of our worries and find solace in the simple beauty that surrounds us. By embracing mindfulness, we can fully appreciate the sights, sounds, and sensations that nature presents, allowing us to cultivate a sense of peace and harmony within ourselves.

In this subchapter, we guide our readers through various mindfulness techniques that can enhance their nature meditation practice. We explore the power of breath awareness, encouraging individuals to focus on their inhalations and exhalations as they absorb the natural environment around them. We also delve into the concept of body scanning, where one mindfully explores the physical sensations experienced during nature meditation, fostering a deeper connection with the present moment.

Moreover, we discuss the importance of cultivating gratitude and a sense of interconnectedness with nature. By acknowledging and appreciating the intricate web of life that surrounds us, we can tap into a wellspring of inner peace and contentment. We provide practical exercises and reflective prompts that encourage individuals to develop a mindful perspective towards the natural world, fostering a sense of harmony and respect for all living beings.

Ultimately, "Earth's Healing Touch" aims to inspire every individual, regardless of their background or lifestyle, to embrace mindfulness as a foundation for their nature meditation practice. By doing so, they can discover the transformative power of the natural world, finding inner peace and a deep connection to the peace of nature that has the potential to heal and rejuvenate their mind, body, and spirit.

Practicing mindfulness in everyday activities

In our fast-paced and hectic modern lives, finding inner peace can often feel like an elusive goal. However, it is possible to cultivate a sense of calm and serenity even amidst the chaos. One powerful tool that can help us achieve this is mindfulness.

Mindfulness is the practice of bringing our full attention to the present moment, without judgment. It allows us to fully engage with our experiences, both pleasant and unpleasant, and helps us develop a deeper connection with ourselves and the world around us. One of the most beautiful ways to incorporate mindfulness into our lives is by infusing it into our everyday activities.

Imagine waking up in the morning and instead of rushing through your morning routine, you take a few moments to simply be present. As you brush your teeth, feel the coolness of the water on your skin and the sensation of the bristles against your teeth. Notice the minty taste of the toothpaste and the sound of the brush against your teeth. By paying attention to these small details, you are fully immersed in the experience, bringing a sense of peace and calm to your morning routine.

Throughout the day, there are countless opportunities to practice mindfulness in our everyday activities. Whether it's sipping a cup of tea, washing dishes, or walking in nature, we can choose to be fully present and engage all our senses. When we eat, for example, we can savor each bite, noticing the flavors, textures, and aromas. By doing so, we not only nourish our bodies but also cultivate a deep appreciation for the simple joys of life.

Nature, in particular, offers a unique opportunity for practicing mindfulness and finding inner peace. Take a moment to step outside and immerse yourself in the beauty of the natural world. Feel the warmth of the sun on your skin, listen to the birds singing, and breathe in the fresh, crisp air. As you walk through a park or forest, be aware of the sensation of the earth beneath your feet and the rustling of leaves in the wind. By connecting with nature in this way, you will discover a sense of peace and harmony that can be truly transformative.

In conclusion, incorporating mindfulness into our everyday activities is a powerful tool for finding inner peace and cultivating a deeper connection with the natural world. By bringing our full attention to the present moment, we can experience a sense of calm and serenity even amidst the chaos of daily life. So, take a moment to pause, breathe, and fully engage with the world around you. Allow the peace of nature to envelop you and discover the immense beauty that lies within and around you.

Applying mindfulness techniques while immersing in nature

In our fast-paced and technology-driven world, finding inner peace can often feel like a distant dream. However, nature has always been a source of solace and tranquility, offering a sanctuary where we can reconnect with ourselves and find a sense of calm. By applying mindfulness techniques while immersing in nature, we can unlock the profound healing powers that the natural world has to offer.

Mindfulness is the practice of being fully present in the moment, without judgment or attachment. When we bring this awareness to our experiences in nature, we can deepen our connection with the world around us and discover a profound sense of peace and harmony.

One technique to cultivate mindfulness in nature is to engage all our senses. As we walk through a forest, for example, we can pay attention to the feeling of the earth beneath our feet, the sound of birds singing in the trees, the scent of pine needles, and the sight of sunlight filtering through the leaves. By fully immersing ourselves in the present moment, we allow nature to speak to us in its own language, awakening our senses and calming our minds.

Another technique is to practice mindful breathing. By focusing on our breath, we can anchor ourselves in the present moment and let go of any worries or distractions. As we inhale deeply, we can imagine breathing in the fresh, revitalizing energy of nature, and as we exhale, we can release any tension or negativity. This simple act of conscious breathing can help us find balance and serenity, even amidst the chaos of our daily lives.

Additionally, we can practice mindful walking in nature. Instead of rushing through our hikes or walks, we can slow down and pay attention to each step we take. With each footfall, we can feel the connection between our bodies and the earth, grounding ourselves in the present moment. As we walk mindfully, we can also observe the beauty and intricacies of nature, allowing it to fill our hearts with gratitude and awe.

By applying mindfulness techniques while immersing in nature, we can tap into the transformative power of the natural world. Whether we are seeking solace, seeking a break from the fast-paced world, or simply yearning to reconnect with our true selves, nature offers the perfect sanctuary. Let us embrace the peace of nature and allow it to heal our souls, one mindful breath at a time.

Chapter 2: Preparation for Nature Meditation

Choosing the Right Outdoor Environment

When seeking solace and peace of mind, there is no greater sanctuary than the embrace of nature. The natural world has an innate ability to heal our weary souls and rejuvenate our spirits. However, not all outdoor environments are created equal when it comes to finding inner peace. In this subchapter, we will explore the art of choosing the right outdoor environment to enhance our connection with nature and experience true tranquility.

First and foremost, it is essential to understand that each individual has unique preferences and needs when it comes to finding peace in nature. Some may find solace in the gentle rustling of leaves in a forest, while others may seek the calming waves of the ocean. Take the time to reflect on what aspects of nature resonate with you the most, and identify the specific environments that align with your preferences.

Consider the geography of your surroundings. Are you more drawn to the majestic mountains, the serene lakes, or the vibrant meadows? Each landscape has its own unique energy, and being aware of your preferences can help you choose the perfect outdoor environment for your peace-seeking journey.

Furthermore, pay attention to the season and weather conditions. For some, the crisp air and falling leaves of autumn create an atmosphere of tranquility, while others may find solace in the warmth and brightness of a sunny summer day. By aligning yourself with the natural rhythms of the seasons, you can enhance your connection with the environment and find inner peace more effortlessly.

Another crucial aspect to consider is the level of seclusion you desire. Some individuals find peace in the solitude and serenity of remote locations, away from the hustle and bustle of daily life. Others may find comfort in the company of like-minded individuals, sharing their love for nature. Reflect on your personal preferences and choose an outdoor environment that aligns with your desired level of solitude.

Finally, remember that the right outdoor environment for finding inner peace may change over time. As we grow and evolve, our preferences and needs may shift. Be open to exploring new environments, trying new activities, and embracing new experiences in nature. Sometimes, the most unexpected places can offer the greatest peace.

In conclusion, choosing the right outdoor environment is a deeply personal and introspective process. By reflecting on your preferences, geographical surroundings, seasonal influences, and desired level of seclusion, you can find an environment that resonates with your soul and provides the peace of nature you seek. Embrace the beauty of the natural world, and let it heal your mind, body, and spirit.

Identifying suitable natural settings for meditation

Subchapter: Identifying Suitable Natural Settings for Meditation

Introduction:
In our fast-paced and technology-driven world, finding inner peace has become a priority for many individuals seeking solace and tranquility. One of the most effective ways to achieve this is through meditation, which allows us to reconnect with ourselves and nature. This subchapter aims to guide individuals from all walks of life in identifying suitable natural settings for their meditation practice, tapping into the incredible healing power of the Earth.

Exploring the Diversity of Natural Settings:
Nature offers a wide range of environments that can enhance your meditation experience. From lush forests and serene meadows to majestic mountains and tranquil beaches, each setting carries its own unique energy and atmosphere. By identifying the natural settings that resonate with you, you can create a harmonious space that fosters peace and tranquility.

The Power of Forests:
Forests have long been cherished as sacred spaces for meditation and self-reflection. The gentle rustling of leaves, the scent of earth, and the vibrant green hues all contribute to a serene atmosphere. Forests provide a sanctuary where you can immerse yourself in the interconnectedness of all living beings, allowing you to find solace and peace within.

The Serenity of Water:
Water, in all its forms, holds a deep sense of tranquility that can soothe

the soul. Whether it's a calm lake, a flowing river, or the vastness of the ocean, the rhythmic sounds and movement of water can help quiet the mind and create a sense of inner peace. Find a spot near water, listen to its melodies, and let it wash away your worries, leaving you feeling refreshed and rejuvenated.

Embracing the Mountains:
For those seeking a sense of grounding and strength, mountains are the ideal natural setting for meditation. Their grandeur and stability create an opportunity to connect with the Earth's energy, grounding you in the present moment. As you gaze upon the majestic peaks, you can tap into their resilience and find your own inner strength.

The Tranquility of Gardens:
Even if you live in an urban environment, you can still create a peaceful oasis by cultivating a garden. Whether it's a small balcony filled with potted plants or a larger backyard, gardens offer a space for meditation that is both nurturing and calming. Surround yourself with the vibrant colors and soothing scents of nature, allowing them to guide you towards a state of inner peace.

Conclusion:
Identifying suitable natural settings for meditation is a personal journey that requires self-reflection and exploration. By immersing ourselves in the peace of nature, we can find solace, tranquility, and a deeper connection with ourselves and the world around us. Whether it's the stillness of a forest, the serenity of water, the strength of mountains, or the nurturing embrace of a garden, nature offers a plethora of opportunities for finding inner peace. So, embark on this

journey, embrace the healing touch of Earth, and let the natural world guide you towards a state of profound inner peace.

Considerations for urban dwellers

Living in a bustling city can be an exhilarating experience, with its vibrant energy and endless opportunities. However, amidst the concrete jungle, it is crucial for urban dwellers to remember the importance of connecting with the peace of nature. In this subchapter, we will explore some key considerations for those seeking to find inner peace in the midst of urban chaos.

First and foremost, it is essential to carve out time in your day to immerse yourself in nature. Whether it is a nearby park, a rooftop garden, or even a window box filled with flowers, finding a green space can have a profound impact on your well-being. Take a break from the noise and pollution, and allow the healing power of nature to wash over you. Even a few minutes spent outside can provide a much-needed respite from the stress of city life.

Another consideration is to incorporate mindfulness into your daily routine. Mindfulness is the practice of being fully present in the moment, and it can be a powerful tool for finding inner peace. As you navigate the busy streets, be aware of your surroundings – the sights, sounds, and smells. Take a moment to truly experience them without judgment. By cultivating mindfulness, you can create a sense of calm amidst the chaos.

Additionally, seek out opportunities to engage with the natural world beyond the city limits. Plan day trips to nearby forests, lakes, or mountains. These outings can be a breath of fresh air, both literally and figuratively, allowing you to reconnect with the peace and tranquility that nature offers. Consider joining a local hiking or birdwatching group to further deepen your connection with the natural world.

Finally, do not underestimate the power of bringing nature into your home. Surround yourself with plants, flowers, and natural elements. Create a small sanctuary within your living space, a place where you can retreat to and find solace. Incorporate natural materials such as wood and stone, and fill your surroundings with the soothing sounds of flowing water or gentle music inspired by nature.

In conclusion, urban dwellers must actively seek out opportunities to connect with the peace of nature. By immersing ourselves in green spaces, practicing mindfulness, venturing out into the wilderness, and bringing elements of nature into our homes, we can find inner peace even in the midst of city chaos. Embrace the healing touch of nature and let it guide you towards a more balanced and peaceful existence.

Creating a sacred space in nature

In today's fast-paced and technology-driven world, finding peace and tranquility can be a challenge. The constant noise and distractions can leave us feeling overwhelmed and disconnected from ourselves and the natural world around us. However, there is a simple and powerful solution – creating a sacred space in nature.

A sacred space is a place where we can go to connect with ourselves, find inner peace, and experience the healing touch of Mother Earth. It is a space where we can leave behind the worries and stresses of daily life and immerse ourselves in the beauty and serenity of nature.

The first step in creating a sacred space in nature is to find a location that resonates with you. It could be a secluded spot in a nearby park, a peaceful corner of your backyard, or a hidden gem in the mountains. Wherever it may be, the important thing is that it feels like a sanctuary for you.

Once you have found your sacred space, it's time to create an atmosphere that promotes peace and connection. Start by clearing any debris or clutter from the area and make it inviting. Add elements from nature such as flowers, stones, or plants to enhance the natural beauty of the space. Consider creating a small altar where you can place meaningful objects like crystals or personal mementos.

Now that your sacred space is ready, it's time to engage in mindful practices to fully immerse yourself in the experience. Start by finding a comfortable position and take a few deep breaths to ground yourself. Close your eyes and tune in to the sounds, smells, and sensations around you. Let go of any thoughts or worries and simply be present in the moment.

You can choose to meditate, practice yoga, journal, or simply sit in silence and observe the world around you. Allow yourself to connect with the peace and serenity that nature offers. Feel the gentle breeze on your skin, listen to the rustling leaves, and breathe in the fresh air. Let the healing energy of the earth wash over you and restore your inner balance.

Creating a sacred space in nature is a powerful way to find peace and reconnect with ourselves. It allows us to step away from the chaos of everyday life and tap into the healing touch of the natural world. So, take the time to find your sacred space and let nature guide you on a journey of inner peace and serenity.

Dressing Appropriately for Nature Meditation

When it comes to nature meditation, it is essential to dress appropriately to fully immerse yourself in the peacefulness of the natural world. In this subchapter, we will discuss the importance of dressing mindfully for your nature meditation practice.

First and foremost, comfort should be your top priority when selecting your attire for nature meditation. Choose loose-fitting and breathable clothing that allows for unrestricted movement. This will enable you to fully engage with your surroundings, whether you are sitting, walking, or practicing gentle yoga poses. Avoid tight or constricting clothes that may hinder your ability to relax and enjoy the experience.

Additionally, consider the weather conditions and the environment you will be meditating in. If it is a sunny day, don't forget to protect yourself from harmful UV rays by wearing a wide-brimmed hat and applying sunscreen. In cooler weather, layering your clothing will allow you to adjust your comfort level as needed. Remember, being in harmony with nature means respecting and adapting to its elements.

Choosing natural and sustainable fabrics can also enhance your connection with the natural world. Opt for materials such as organic cotton, hemp, or linen, as they are not only eco-friendly but also allow your skin to breathe. By selecting clothing made from these materials, you are aligning your intentions with the principles of sustainability and respect for the Earth.

Furthermore, consider the colors you wear during your nature meditation practice. Earth tones, such as greens, browns, and blues, can have a calming effect and help you feel more connected to the natural environment. Avoid bright or flashy colors that may distract you or disrupt the serene atmosphere.

Remember that dressing appropriately for nature meditation goes beyond just the physical aspects. It is an opportunity to express your reverence and gratitude for the natural world. As you choose your clothing, reflect on the interconnectedness of all living beings and the role that nature plays in providing us with peace and serenity.

In conclusion, dressing appropriately for nature meditation involves choosing comfortable, weather-appropriate, and sustainable clothing that reflects your connection to the Earth. By being mindful of what you wear, you can enhance your experience and fully embrace the peace and tranquility that nature has to offer. So, take a moment to consider your outfit before heading out to your next nature meditation session, and let the healing touch of the Earth envelop you in its embrace.

Selecting comfortable and weather-appropriate clothing

In our busy lives, it is all too easy to forget the importance of connecting with the natural world. The peace and tranquility that nature offers can do wonders for our mental and emotional well-being. Earth's Healing Touch: Mindful Practices for Finding Inner Peace in the Natural World is a book that aims to guide individuals towards rediscovering their connection with nature and harnessing its healing power.

One crucial aspect of immersing oneself in nature is selecting comfortable and weather-appropriate clothing. While it may seem like a trivial matter, the right clothing can make a significant difference in your overall experience. Whether you are taking a leisurely stroll through a park or embarking on a challenging hike, here are some tips to help you choose the perfect attire.

First and foremost, comfort should be your top priority. Opt for clothing made from breathable and lightweight fabrics, such as cotton or linen, that allow airflow and prevent excessive sweating. This will keep you cool and comfortable, even on hot summer days. Additionally, choose clothing with a relaxed fit that allows for ease of movement. Restrictive clothing can hinder your ability to fully immerse yourself in the natural world.

Furthermore, it is crucial to consider the weather conditions before heading out. If you are venturing into colder climates, layering is key. Start with a moisture-wicking base layer to keep sweat away from your skin. Follow it up with a thermal mid-layer for insulation, and top it off with a waterproof and windproof outer layer to protect you from the elements. Don't forget to wear a hat, gloves, and warm socks to keep extremities cozy.

On the other hand, if you are exploring during warmer months, opt for loose-fitting, light-colored clothing that reflects the sun's rays. Hats with wide brims and sunglasses can provide much-needed shade and protect your eyes from harmful UV rays. Don't forget to apply sunscreen to exposed skin to prevent sunburn.

Remember, the purpose of your attire is not just to protect you but also to enhance your connection with nature. By selecting clothing that is comfortable and weather-appropriate, you can fully immerse yourself in the peace and tranquility of the natural world. So, the next time you embark on an adventure outdoors, choose your attire mindfully, and let nature work its healing touch on your soul.

Importance of proper footwear

In our fast-paced modern lives, it is easy to forget the importance of connecting with nature. Yet, the natural world has an incredible power to heal and restore our inner peace. One simple way to engage with nature is by exploring the great outdoors through hiking, walking, or simply taking a stroll in the park. And when it comes to these activities, the significance of proper footwear cannot be overstated.

Footwear is not just a fashion statement; it plays a crucial role in our overall well-being, especially when we venture into nature. Choosing the right footwear ensures comfort, stability, and protection for our feet, allowing us to fully immerse ourselves in the peace nature has to offer.

Comfort is key when it comes to proper footwear. As we walk or hike, our feet endure constant pressure and impact. Ill-fitting shoes can lead to blisters, foot pain, and even more serious conditions like plantar fasciitis. On the other hand, well-designed and properly fitting shoes provide the necessary support and cushioning, preventing discomfort and allowing us to focus on the tranquility of our surroundings.

Stability is another important factor to consider. Uneven terrains, slippery surfaces, and rocky trails can all pose a challenge to our balance, especially if we are not wearing the right shoes. Shoes with good traction, ankle support, and durable soles help us maintain stability, reducing the risk of slips or falls. By ensuring our feet are secure, we can fully embrace the serenity of nature without worrying about potential accidents.

Lastly, proper footwear protects our feet from various hazards in nature. From sharp rocks to thorns and rough terrains, nature can be unforgiving to exposed feet. The right shoes act as a shield, preventing injuries and allowing us to freely explore our surroundings without fear. Additionally, they can provide insulation against cold or wet conditions, ensuring our feet remain dry and warm, further enhancing our comfort and peace of mind.

In conclusion, when it comes to immersing ourselves in the peace of nature, proper footwear is of utmost importance. By choosing comfortable, stable, and protective shoes, we can fully engage with the natural world, experience its healing touch, and find inner peace. So, the next time you plan a nature excursion, remember to prioritize your footwear selection and allow the wonders of nature to soothe your soul.

Protecting yourself from natural elements

In our modern world, it is easy to forget the power and beauty of nature. We often find ourselves disconnected from the natural world, consumed by the demands of daily life. However, reconnecting with nature can bring us a profound sense of peace and serenity that is often lacking in our busy lives. It is essential to protect ourselves from the elements of nature, as they can both nourish and challenge our well-being.

One of the first steps in protecting ourselves from the natural elements is to understand and respect their power. Nature has a way of reminding us of our place in the world, and it is crucial to approach it with humility and caution. Whether it is the scorching heat of the sun, the frigid cold of winter, or the fury of a thunderstorm, being aware of the potential dangers can help us mitigate them.

When it comes to protecting ourselves from the elements, prevention is key. Dressing appropriately for the weather conditions is essential. Layering clothing can help regulate body temperature, while protective gear such as hats, sunglasscs, and sunscreen can shield us from the harmful rays of the sun. Additionally, it is crucial to stay hydrated and nourished, as nature's elements can quickly deplete our energy and resources.

Seeking shelter is another vital aspect of protecting ourselves from the natural elements. Whether it is finding shade on a scorching summer day or taking cover during a storm, having a safe haven can make all the difference. Taking the time to prepare and plan ahead can ensure that we have access to shelter when we need it most.

Furthermore, it is essential to develop an understanding of our surroundings. Learning about the local climate, weather patterns, and potential hazards can help us make more informed decisions and stay safe. Additionally, being mindful of our impact on the environment can contribute to the preservation of the natural world. By practicing Leave No Trace principles and being mindful of our presence, we can protect both ourselves and the peace of nature.

In conclusion, protecting ourselves from the natural elements is crucial for finding inner peace in the natural world. By understanding the power and beauty of nature, dressing appropriately, seeking shelter, and being mindful of our surroundings, we can embrace the healing touch of the Earth while ensuring our safety. May we all find solace and serenity in the embrace of nature and discover the profound connection it offers.

Gathering Essential Supplies

In our fast-paced and technology-driven world, it is easy to lose touch with the peace and serenity that nature can offer. However, reconnecting with the natural world is essential for finding inner peace and achieving a sense of harmony in our lives. In this subchapter, we will explore the importance of gathering essential supplies to enhance our experience and connection with nature.

When embarking on a journey to find inner peace in the natural world, it is crucial to have the right supplies at hand. These supplies not only ensure our comfort and safety but also enable us to fully immerse ourselves in the beauty and tranquility of nature. Here are some essential items that can help us make the most of our experience:

1. Outdoor Gear: Investing in high-quality outdoor gear, such as comfortable hiking boots, weather-appropriate clothing, and a sturdy backpack, will enable us to explore nature with ease and confidence. This gear ensures that we are prepared for any weather conditions and can fully focus on our connection with the environment.

2. Mindfulness Tools: Carrying mindfulness tools, such as a meditation cushion or a portable yoga mat, can help us create a dedicated space for connecting with nature. These tools allow us to practice mindfulness and find inner peace even in the busiest of outdoor settings.

3. Nature Guidebooks: Having guidebooks that identify local flora and fauna can enhance our experience in nature by deepening our understanding of the natural world. These guidebooks enable us to

appreciate the beauty and intricacy of the environment around us, fostering a greater sense of connection and peace.

4. Journal and Pen: Keeping a journal allows us to reflect on our experiences and emotions while in nature. It provides a space for self-expression and helps us capture the moments of awe and inspiration that we encounter. Writing in a journal can be a cathartic and transformative process, deepening our connection with the peace of nature.

Remember, gathering essential supplies is not about accumulating material possessions but rather about choosing tools that support our connection with the natural world. By carefully selecting the items that resonate with our intentions and values, we can create a space for inner peace and harmony in the embrace of nature's healing touch.

Whether we are embarking on a short hike, spending a weekend camping trip, or simply taking a walk in the park, having the right supplies can make all the difference in our journey towards finding inner peace in the natural world. So, pack your gear, equip yourself with mindfulness tools, and embrace the beauty that surrounds you. Let nature's healing touch guide you towards the peace you seek.

Recommended items to bring on your nature meditation journey

When embarking on a nature meditation journey, it is essential to be prepared and equipped with the necessary tools to enhance your experience and find inner peace in the natural world. In this subchapter, we will explore some recommended items that can greatly contribute to your journey towards tranquility and connection with nature.

1. Comfortable Clothing: Nature meditation often involves sitting or walking for extended periods. It is crucial to wear loose, comfortable clothing that allows you to move freely and doesn't restrict your breathing. Additionally, consider dressing in layers to adjust to changing weather conditions and bring a hat and sunglasses to protect yourself from the sun.

2. A Meditation Cushion or Mat: Sitting on the ground can sometimes be uncomfortable, especially on uneven terrain. A meditation cushion or mat provides support, allowing you to maintain a relaxed and focused posture. It can also serve as a portable meditation space, creating a designated area for your practice.

3. Water Bottle: Staying hydrated is crucial during any outdoor activity, including nature meditation. Remember to bring a reusable water bottle filled with fresh water to keep yourself hydrated throughout your journey. Drinking water also helps to stay mindful and present during your meditation practice.

4. Journal and Pen: Nature meditation often brings about moments of clarity and inspiration. Having a journal and pen handy allows you to capture these insights and reflections, preserving them for future

contemplation. Writing down your thoughts can also serve as a form of therapy and self-exploration.

5. Binoculars or Camera: Nature is full of wonders and surprises. Bringing binoculars or a camera enables you to observe and capture the intricate details of the natural world. Whether it's a vibrant bird or a delicate flower, these tools allow you to deepen your connection with nature and appreciate its beauty in a more profound way.

6. Insect Repellent and Sunscreen: Depending on the location and time of year, insects and the sun's rays can pose challenges to your meditation experience. Be sure to bring insect repellent to ward off mosquitoes and ticks. Applying sunscreen protects your skin from harmful UV rays, ensuring your journey remains comfortable and safe.

By embracing these recommended items, you can enhance your nature meditation journey and fully immerse yourself in the peace and tranquility of the natural world. Remember, the purpose of these items is to support your practice, allowing you to find inner peace and experience the healing touch of the Earth.

Packing light and efficiently

When embarking on a journey into the peaceful embrace of nature, it is essential to travel lightly and efficiently. The art of packing efficiently allows us to focus on the beauty around us rather than being weighed down by unnecessary baggage. In this subchapter, we will explore practical tips and strategies to help you pack light and make the most of your time in nature.

1. Prioritize the Essentials: Begin by making a list of essential items you will need for your trip. This includes clothing suitable for the weather, toiletries, and any medication you may require. Remember, the goal is to pack light, so be mindful of what you truly need.

2. Choose Versatile Clothing: Select clothing items that can be layered or mixed and matched. Opt for lightweight and quick-drying fabrics, as these are more practical in outdoor settings. Consider the weather conditions and pack accordingly, ensuring you have appropriate attire for both warm and cold climates.

3. Minimize Toiletries: Instead of carrying full-sized toiletry bottles, invest in travel-sized containers or decant your favorite products into smaller bottles. This will save space and reduce weight. Additionally, opt for multi-purpose items such as a combination shampoo and conditioner to further streamline your packing.

4. Pack Smartly: Utilize packing cubes or compression bags to maximize space within your luggage. Rolling clothes instead of folding them can also save space and prevent wrinkles. Place heavier items at the bottom of your bag and distribute weight evenly to maintain balance and comfort while carrying.

5. Leave Room for Souvenirs: If you anticipate bringing back souvenirs or mementos from your trip, ensure you have some extra space in your luggage. This way, you won't have to worry about sacrificing any of your belongings or purchasing an additional bag.

By packing light and efficiently, you not only reduce physical burden but also create space for a peaceful and freeing experience in nature. As you embark on your journey, remember that the true treasures lie in the sights, sounds, and sensations of the natural world, not in the material possessions we carry with us.

So, take a deep breath, embrace the simplicity of packing light, and allow yourself to fully immerse in the peace nature has to offer.

Eco-friendly practices for nature meditation supplies

In today's fast-paced and technology-driven world, finding inner peace and tranquility can seem like an elusive goal. However, one of the most effective and fulfilling ways to reconnect with ourselves and the natural world is through nature meditation. By immersing ourselves in the beauty and serenity of the environment, we can find solace, clarity, and a profound sense of peace.

When embarking on a journey of nature meditation, it is essential to consider the impact our practices have on the environment. In order to fully align with the principles of mindfulness and sustainability, incorporating eco-friendly practices into our nature meditation supplies is crucial.

One of the first steps towards an eco-friendly approach is to choose sustainable materials for your meditation tools. Replace synthetic or plastic items with those made from natural materials such as bamboo, wood, or organic cotton. These materials have a lower environmental impact and are biodegradable, ensuring that they do not contribute to pollution or waste.

Another eco-conscious choice is to opt for locally sourced or ethically made products. By supporting local artisans or companies that prioritize fair trade practices, we can contribute to sustainable economies and reduce our carbon footprint. Additionally, choosing handmade or artisanal items adds a personal touch to our meditation practice, creating a deeper connection between ourselves and the natural world.

Furthermore, it is important to minimize waste in our nature meditation practice. Instead of disposable items, invest in reusable alternatives. For instance, using a refillable water bottle instead of single-use plastic bottles or carrying a reusable cloth bag for your supplies can significantly reduce your environmental impact.

In addition to sustainable materials and reducing waste, it is crucial to respect and preserve the natural surroundings during our meditation sessions. Follow the principles of Leave No Trace, ensuring that you leave the area as you found it. Avoid damaging plants or disturbing wildlife, and refrain from picking flowers or removing natural elements from their environment.

By adopting these eco-friendly practices for nature meditation supplies, we can deepen our connection with the natural world while preserving and protecting it. Remember, the earth's healing touch is not only for our benefit, but also for the generations to come. Let us embrace these mindful practices and become stewards of the earth, finding peace in nature while ensuring its preservation for all.

Chapter 3: Techniques for Immersing in Nature Meditation

Breath Awareness in Nature

Breath Awareness in Nature: Finding Inner Peace through the Healing Power of the Natural World

In our fast-paced, technology-driven lives, it's easy to become disconnected from the world around us. We often find ourselves overwhelmed by stress, anxiety, and the constant demands of modern living. But deep within each of us lies a longing for peace and tranquility, a desire to connect with something greater than ourselves. This is where the healing power of nature comes in.

Nature has a unique ability to restore our sense of balance and inner peace. When we immerse ourselves in the beauty of the natural world, we are reminded of the simple joys and wonders of life. Breath awareness in nature is a practice that can help us tap into this healing energy and find solace amidst the chaos.

The practice of breath awareness involves focusing our attention on our breath, using it as an anchor to bring us into the present moment. When we combine this practice with the serene and peaceful surroundings of nature, the effects are truly transformative.

Imagine yourself sitting by a babbling brook, surrounded by lush greenery and the gentle rustling of leaves. As you become aware of your breath, you begin to feel a sense of calm and stillness envelop you.

The worries and thoughts that once consumed your mind start to fade away, replaced by a deep sense of peace and connectedness.

Nature has a way of slowing us down, allowing us to step out of the constant rush of life and into a state of mindfulness. By focusing on our breath, we become attuned to the rhythm of nature itself. We notice the ebb and flow of the wind, the chirping of birds, and the gentle hum of insects. We become aware of the interconnectedness of all living beings and our place within this vast and beautiful world.

Breath awareness in nature is a practice that can be incorporated into our daily lives, even when we can't physically be in nature. Whether it's taking a few moments to sit in a park, walking barefoot on grass, or simply gazing at a potted plant, these small acts can bring us closer to the peace and serenity of the natural world.

So, take a moment to pause and breathe. Allow yourself to be fully present in this moment, surrounded by the peace of nature. Let the healing touch of the Earth guide you towards inner peace and a renewed sense of self. Embrace the beauty and tranquility that nature offers, and you will find that the path to inner peace lies just beyond your next breath.

Focusing on the breath to find grounding and presence

In our fast-paced and chaotic world, finding inner peace and tranquility can sometimes feel like an impossible task. However, one of the most powerful tools we have at our disposal is always within reach - our breath. By simply tuning into our breath and focusing on it, we can find grounding and presence amidst the chaos, reconnecting with the peace of nature that surrounds us.

When we consciously pay attention to our breath, we invite ourselves into the present moment. The breath acts as an anchor, grounding us in the here and now. Inhaling deeply, we can feel the air filling our lungs, awakening our senses to the beauty and stillness of the natural world. Exhaling, we release any tension or worries, allowing ourselves to fully immerse in the present moment.

One powerful technique to enhance our connection with the breath and nature is mindful breathing. Find a peaceful spot in nature, perhaps a quiet park or a serene forest, and take a moment to sit comfortably. Close your eyes and bring your attention to your breath. Notice the sensation of the air entering and leaving your body. Feel the rise and fall of your chest as you inhale and exhale. As you continue to breathe, let go of any thoughts or distractions, allowing yourself to fully surrender to the present moment.

As you focus on your breath, you may begin to notice the sounds of nature around you - the gentle rustling of leaves, the chirping of birds, or the soft babbling of a nearby stream. Allow these sounds to further deepen your connection to the peace of nature. As you inhale, imagine that you are breathing in the vibrant energy of the natural world, filling your body with a sense of calm and tranquility. As you exhale, visualize releasing any stress or worries, allowing them to dissolve into the earth.

By practicing this mindful breathing exercise regularly, we can cultivate a deep sense of grounding and presence. We become more attuned to the peace of nature that surrounds us, and in turn, find inner peace within ourselves. The breath becomes our guide, gently reminding us to slow down, let go, and fully embrace the beauty and serenity of the natural world.

In the hustle and bustle of everyday life, it's easy to lose sight of the peace that nature offers us. However, by focusing on our breath and practicing mindful breathing, we can always find our way back to the grounding and presence that the natural world provides. Take a moment each day to reconnect with your breath and the peace of nature, and watch as your inner peace blossoms, bringing harmony and tranquility to your life.

Combining breath awareness with observing nature's rhythms

In our fast-paced, modern lives, finding inner peace has become increasingly challenging. We find ourselves constantly bombarded with information, distractions, and stressors that seem to never cease. But amidst the chaos, there is a sanctuary where peace can always be found - nature. The soothing sounds of a babbling brook, the gentle rustling of leaves, and the vibrant colors of a sunset all have the power to transport us to a place of calm and serenity.

In the subchapter titled "Combining Breath Awareness with Observing Nature's Rhythms," we delve into the profound connection between breath awareness and the rhythms of nature. This practice is a gateway to experiencing the healing power of nature and finding inner peace in the process.

Breath awareness is a fundamental mindfulness technique that involves bringing our attention to the present moment by focusing on our breath. It is a simple yet powerful practice that allows us to anchor our awareness in the present, quieting the noise of our thoughts and worries. When we combine this practice with observing nature's rhythms, we enhance our ability to connect deeply with the world around us.

Nature's rhythms are a constant reminder of the interconnectedness of all living beings. From the ebb and flow of the tides to the cycle of the seasons, nature follows a harmonious pattern that we can learn from. By observing and aligning our breath with these natural rhythms, we tap into the wisdom of the earth and find ourselves in a state of profound peace.

Imagine sitting by a tranquil lake, the gentle breeze caressing your face, as you synchronize your breath with the rhythmic lapping of the water against the shore. With each inhale and exhale, you feel your body and mind becoming attuned to the natural world. Your worries and anxieties dissipate, and you are fully present in the moment, experiencing the peace and tranquility that nature offers.

The practice of combining breath awareness with observing nature's rhythms is accessible to everyone, regardless of age or background. It requires only a willingness to step outside, to be still, and to listen. Whether you find solace in a bustling city park or the vast expanse of a forest, nature has the power to heal and restore.

In "Earth's Healing Touch: Mindful Practices for Finding Inner Peace in the Natural World," we invite you to embark on a transformative journey of self-discovery through the practice of combining breath awareness with observing nature's rhythms. By cultivating a deep connection with the natural world, you will find that the peace you seek is within reach, waiting to be discovered amidst the wonders of the earth.

Cultivating a sense of calm through breath awareness

In today's fast-paced and ever-connected world, finding inner peace can sometimes feel like an elusive goal. However, amidst the chaos, there is a powerful tool that can help us reconnect with our inner selves and find a sense of calm – breath awareness. This subchapter explores how we can cultivate a deep sense of peace by harnessing the power of our breath in the embrace of nature.

Breath awareness is a simple yet profound practice that involves consciously paying attention to our breath. By focusing our attention on the inhales and exhales, we can anchor ourselves in the present moment and create a space for tranquility to arise. When combined with the peace of nature, the effects can be truly transformative.

Nature has a unique ability to soothe our souls and bring us back to a state of balance. The gentle rustling of leaves, the melodious chirping of birds, and the rhythmic crashing of waves all serve as reminders of the inherent harmony that exists in the natural world. By immersing ourselves in these peaceful surroundings, we open ourselves up to the healing touch of Earth, allowing it to guide us on a journey towards inner peace.

As we sit in a serene natural setting, we can begin our breath awareness practice. Closing our eyes, we bring our attention to the sensation of the breath entering and leaving our bodies. With each inhale, we imagine drawing in the freshness and vitality of the natural world, filling our beings with a sense of tranquility. With each exhale, we release any tension or worries, allowing them to melt away into the earth beneath us.

Through this mindful practice, we learn to cultivate a sense of calm that transcends the chaos of everyday life. By connecting with our breath and the peace of nature, we tap into a wellspring of inner peace that resides within each and every one of us. This newfound sense of tranquility can have profound effects on our mental, emotional, and physical well-being.

In a world that often pulls us in a million different directions, cultivating a sense of calm through breath awareness and the peace of nature becomes an invaluable tool for finding inner peace. As we embark on this journey, let us remember that the path to tranquility lies within us, waiting to be discovered through the power of our breath and the healing touch of Earth.

Sensory Immersion

Sensory Immersion: Awakening Your Senses to the Healing Power of Nature

In our fast-paced, technologically driven world, finding inner peace and tranquility can often feel like an elusive goal. However, there is a profound solution that lies right at our fingertips, waiting to be rediscovered – the healing power of nature. In this subchapter, we will explore the concept of sensory immersion and how it can help us find inner peace amidst the chaos of everyday life.

Sensory immersion is the practice of fully engaging our senses in the natural world around us. It is a way to reconnect with the beauty and serenity of nature, allowing it to calm our minds, rejuvenate our spirits, and restore our sense of inner peace. By immersing ourselves in the sights, sounds, smells, tastes, and textures of nature, we awaken our senses to the healing potential that lies within.

Imagine walking through a lush forest, feeling the soft breeze brush against your skin and the gentle caress of sunlight filtering through the leaves above. You hear the melodic symphony of birdsong, the soothing rhythm of a babbling brook, and the rustling of leaves underfoot. The scent of damp earth, blooming flowers, and fresh pine fills the air, while the taste of crisp, clean water from a natural spring refreshes your palate. As you touch the rough bark of a tree or the smooth petals of a flower, you become fully present in the moment, immersed in the peaceful embrace of nature.

Sensory immersion allows us to escape the noise and distractions of modern life, and instead, tune into the serenity and harmony of the natural world. It provides a respite for our overstimulated minds and a sanctuary for our weary souls. Through this practice, we can experience a profound sense of interconnectedness, recognizing that we are an integral part of the larger web of life.

Whether you live in a bustling city or a remote countryside, sensory immersion is accessible to everyone. It can be as simple as taking a mindful walk in a local park, meditating by the ocean, or tending to a garden. By intentionally engaging our senses and opening ourselves to the peace of nature, we invite its healing touch into our lives.

In the following chapters, we will delve deeper into various mindful practices that harness the power of sensory immersion. From forest bathing to nature journaling, each practice offers a unique way to connect with the natural world and find inner peace. So, take a deep breath, step outside, and embark on a journey of sensory immersion – let the healing power of nature guide you towards a more peaceful and harmonious existence.

Engaging all five senses to deepen the nature meditation experience

In our fast-paced and technology-driven world, it's easy to lose touch with the natural world and the profound sense of peace and tranquility it can offer. However, by engaging all five senses, we can deepen our nature meditation experience and reconnect with the healing power of the Earth. In this subchapter, we will explore how each of our senses can be harnessed to enhance our connection with nature and find inner peace.

Sight is often the sense we rely on most, but it can also be the one that distracts us from being fully present. To truly engage with nature, try softening your gaze and noticing the intricate details of your surroundings. Observe the colors, shapes, and movements of plants and animals, allowing yourself to become fully absorbed in the beauty of the natural world.

Sound is another powerful tool for deepening your nature meditation experience. Close your eyes and listen to the rhythmic symphony of birdsong, rustling leaves, or the gentle flow of a nearby stream. Allow these sounds to wash over you, immersing yourself in the soothing harmony of nature's melodies.

Touch is a sense often overlooked in nature meditation, but it can be incredibly grounding. Take off your shoes and feel the earth beneath your feet, noticing its texture and temperature. Run your fingers along the rough bark of a tree or dip your hand into a cool stream. By physically connecting with nature, you can awaken a sense of connectedness and peace within yourself.

Taste can also play a role in deepening your nature meditation experience. Take a moment to enjoy a simple snack or drink while sitting in a serene natural setting. Savor each bite or sip, allowing yourself to fully experience the flavors and textures. By engaging your sense of taste, you can bring a sense of mindfulness and appreciation to your nature meditation practice.

Finally, scent can be a powerful trigger for relaxation and peace. Breathe in deeply, taking in the subtle aromas of flowers, trees, and the earth itself. Allow these scents to transport you, creating a deeper sense of presence and connection to the natural world.

By engaging all five senses, we can unlock the full potential of our nature meditation practice and find inner peace in the embrace of the Earth. Whether you choose to focus on one sense at a time or incorporate them all, the key is to be fully present in the moment and open to the wonders of the natural world. Embrace the healing touch of the Earth and let it guide you towards a more peaceful and connected way of being.

Noticing the sounds, smells, and textures of nature

In our fast-paced modern lives, it's easy to become disconnected from the natural world around us. We often rush from one task to another, barely taking the time to appreciate the beauty and tranquility that nature offers. However, by cultivating the practice of noticing the sounds, smells, and textures of nature, we can tap into a profound sense of peace and find solace in the embrace of Mother Earth.

When we venture into nature, we are greeted by a symphony of sounds. The gentle rustling of leaves, the melodious chirping of birds, and the soothing babbling of a nearby stream all invite us to tune in and listen. By taking a moment to truly notice these sounds, we can quiet our minds and enter a state of deep relaxation. Close your eyes and let the sounds envelop you, becoming one with the harmonious rhythm of nature.

Nature also has an array of captivating smells that can transport us to a place of serenity. The crisp scent of pine needles, the sweet aroma of wildflowers, or the earthy fragrance after rainfall can awaken our senses and ignite a sense of peace within. Explore the scents around you, breathe them in deeply, and let them remind you of the simple joys that nature provides.

As we venture into nature, we encounter a myriad of textures that awaken our tactile senses. The rough bark of a tree, the velvety petals of a flower, or the softness of moss beneath our feet all offer opportunities for mindful connection. Take a moment to touch and feel the textures of nature, allowing them to ground you and bring you into the present moment. Let your fingertips guide you along the path of nature's wonders.

Noticing the sounds, smells, and textures of nature is an invitation to be fully present. It is a practice that allows us to let go of our worries, anxieties, and stresses, and instead, reconnect with the peace that nature graciously offers. Whether you find solace in the whispering wind, the scent of blooming flowers, or the touch of cool, dewy grass, nature is always there, waiting to embrace you and provide you with a profound sense of inner peace.

So, take a moment today to step outside and immerse yourself in the symphony of nature. Allow yourself to be fully present, noticing the sounds, smells, and textures that surround you. In doing so, you will find that the peace of nature becomes a sanctuary for your soul, a place where worries fade and true inner peace can be found. Embrace the healing touch of Earth and let it guide you on a journey towards harmony and tranquility.

Developing a heightened sense of awareness through sensory immersion

In our fast-paced and technology-driven world, it is easy to become disconnected from the natural world around us. We often find ourselves caught up in the hustle and bustle of daily life, forgetting to take a moment to appreciate the beauty and tranquility that nature has to offer. However, by developing a heightened sense of awareness through sensory immersion, we can reestablish our connection with the earth and find inner peace in the process.

Sensory immersion involves engaging all our senses – sight, hearing, touch, smell, and taste – to fully experience and appreciate the natural world. By consciously tuning into these senses, we can become more present in the moment and develop a deeper understanding of our surroundings. This practice can lead to a profound sense of peace and connection with nature.

One way to begin developing a heightened sense of awareness is through mindful walks in nature. Take a leisurely stroll through a forest, a park, or along a beach, and pay attention to the sights, sounds, and smells around you. Notice the vibrant colors of the flowers, the melody of the birdsong, and the refreshing scent of the earth. Engage your sense of touch by feeling the texture of tree bark or the coolness of a stream. By immersing yourself in these sensory experiences, you will begin to feel a sense of peace and tranquility wash over you.

Another powerful tool for sensory immersion is meditation. Find a quiet spot in nature, sit down, and close your eyes. As you focus on your breath, allow yourself to become fully aware of the sensations around you. Feel the warmth of the sun on your skin, listen to the gentle rustling of leaves, and inhale the crisp scent of the air. By opening yourself up to these sensory experiences, you can achieve a state of deep relaxation and connection with the natural world.

In conclusion, developing a heightened sense of awareness through sensory immersion is a powerful practice that can bring us closer to nature and provide us with inner peace. By engaging all our senses and fully experiencing the beauty and tranquility of the natural world, we can reconnect with the earth and find solace in its embrace. So, take a moment to immerse yourself in the sights, sounds, and smells of nature – you may just find that it brings you the peace you have been seeking.

Nature-Based Mindfulness Practices

In today's fast-paced and digitally-driven world, finding inner peace can often feel like an elusive goal. However, there is a powerful and accessible solution that is right at our fingertips – the healing touch of nature. In this subchapter, we will explore the transformative practice of nature-based mindfulness, which allows us to reconnect with the peace and tranquility that can only be found in the natural world.

Nature has always been a source of solace and inspiration for humanity. Whether it is the gentle rustle of leaves in a forest, the rhythmic crashing of waves on a beach, or the vibrant colors of a sunrise, nature has a way of captivating our senses and bringing us into the present moment. By engaging with the natural world mindfully, we can tap into its innate healing properties and cultivate a deep sense of inner peace.

One of the simplest ways to practice nature-based mindfulness is through mindful walking. Instead of rushing through our daily walks, we can slow down and pay attention to the sensations in our body as we move. We can feel the earth beneath our feet, the warm sun on our skin, and the cool breeze against our face. By bringing our awareness to these physical sensations, we become grounded in the present and open ourselves up to the peace that nature offers.

Another powerful practice is mindful observation. Find a quiet spot in nature and simply observe the world around you. Notice the intricate patterns of a flower, the graceful flight of a bird, or the constant ebb and flow of a river. As you observe, allow your thoughts to gently drift away, and fully immerse yourself in the beauty and serenity of the natural world. This practice can be particularly helpful for those seeking peace in nature, as it allows us to let go of our worries and connect with something greater than ourselves.

Nature-based mindfulness practices not only bring peace to our minds and bodies but also deepen our connection with the natural world. As we become more attuned to nature's rhythms and cycles, we develop a sense of belonging and interconnectedness. We realize that we are not separate from nature but rather an integral part of it. This understanding can be profoundly transformative, leading to a sense of peace that extends beyond our individual selves.

In conclusion, nature-based mindfulness practices offer a powerful pathway to finding inner peace in the natural world. By engaging with nature mindfully, we can reconnect with our true selves and tap into the peace that nature effortlessly provides. So, whether you are seeking solace, inspiration, or a deeper connection with the world around you, let the healing touch of nature guide you on your journey towards inner peace.

Walking meditation in nature

Walking meditation in nature is a powerful practice that allows us to connect deeply with the natural world and find inner peace. In today's fast-paced and stressful society, taking the time to immerse ourselves in nature can have a profound healing effect on our well-being.

The concept of walking meditation involves bringing our full awareness to the present moment as we engage in the simple act of walking. By doing this in nature, we can fully appreciate the beauty and tranquility that surrounds us. Whether it's a serene forest, a picturesque beach, or a vibrant garden, nature has a way of soothing our souls and restoring a sense of peace within us.

As we embark on a walking meditation in nature, it's essential to set aside any distractions and fully engage our senses. Begin by taking a few deep breaths, feeling the air fill your lungs and exhaling any tension or stress. Allow your body to relax and your mind to become calm.

As you start walking, pay attention to each step you take. Notice how your feet make contact with the ground, the texture of the earth beneath you, and the sensations that arise with each movement. Let go of any thoughts or worries and simply be present in the moment.

As you continue walking, observe your surroundings with curiosity and awe. Take in the vibrant colors of the flowers, the gentle rustling of leaves, or the sound of birds singing. Feel the warmth of the sun on your skin or the cool breeze against your face. Allow yourself to fully connect with the peace and beauty of nature.

Walking meditation in nature not only helps us find inner peace but also fosters a deeper connection with the Earth. It reminds us that we are part of a vast and interconnected web of life. As we walk mindfully, we can cultivate a sense of gratitude and reverence for the natural world, which in turn nourishes our souls.

So, whether you are seeking solace, a break from the hectic pace of life, or simply a way to connect with nature, walking meditation is a practice that can bring you closer to finding inner peace. Take the time to step outside, breathe in the fresh air, and let the healing touch of the Earth guide you towards a more peaceful and fulfilling life.

Forest bathing: Reconnecting with the healing power of trees

Forest bathing, also known as Shinrin-yoku, is a practice that encourages us to reconnect with the healing power of trees and nature. In today's fast-paced and technology-driven world, we often find ourselves disconnected from the natural world around us. We spend most of our time indoors, glued to screens, and surrounded by concrete jungles. But deep within us, there is an innate longing for peace and tranquility that can only be found in nature.

Forest bathing offers us an opportunity to fulfill that longing and find inner peace through immersing ourselves in the natural world. It is a simple yet profound practice that involves spending time in forests, consciously engaging with nature, and allowing ourselves to be fully present in the moment.

When we practice forest bathing, we engage all our senses to fully experience the forest. We listen to the rustling of leaves, the chirping of birds, and the sound of flowing water. We feel the texture of tree bark, the softness of moss, and the coolness of the earth beneath our feet. We breathe in the fresh, oxygen-rich air, allowing it to rejuvenate our bodies and minds.

Studies have shown that spending time in nature, especially in forests, has numerous health benefits. Forest bathing has been proven to reduce stress, lower blood pressure, boost the immune system, and improve overall well-being. The phytoncides released by trees have even been found to enhance our immune function, helping us fight off diseases and infections.

But forest bathing is not just about the physical benefits; it is also a practice that nourishes our souls. The stillness and serenity of the forest allow us to find inner peace and connect with something greater than ourselves. In the presence of trees, we can let go of our worries, fears, and anxieties, and experience a deep sense of calm and tranquility.

Forest bathing is a practice that is accessible to everyone, regardless of their age or physical abilities. Whether it's a short walk in a local park or a hike in a vast forest, the healing power of trees is available to all who seek it. So, let us step away from our screens, venture into the natural world, and allow the healing touch of the Earth to bring us inner peace and harmony.

Nature journaling for reflection and self-discovery

Nature journaling is a powerful tool that allows us to connect with the natural world on a deeper level, while also enabling us to reflect on our own thoughts and emotions. In this subchapter, we will explore how nature journaling can serve as a pathway to self-discovery and inner peace.

When we immerse ourselves in the serenity of nature, our minds become still, and our senses awaken to the beauty that surrounds us. Nature journaling encourages us to observe and appreciate the intricate details of the natural world, from the delicate petals of a flower to the majestic flight of a bird. As we record these observations in our journals, we become more attuned to the present moment, grounding ourselves in the peace and tranquility of nature.

Through nature journaling, we also gain a greater understanding of ourselves. As we reflect on our experiences in nature, we begin to uncover our own thoughts, emotions, and beliefs. The act of putting pen to paper allows us to articulate our innermost thoughts and feelings, providing us with a safe space for self-expression and self-discovery. By engaging in this reflective practice, we can gain insights into our own values, aspirations, and personal growth.

Nature journaling also fosters a sense of interconnectedness with the natural world. As we observe and record the cycles of nature, we begin to recognize the patterns and rhythms that exist both in the external world and within ourselves. This awareness of our connection to nature can bring us a profound sense of peace and harmony, reminding us that we are a part of something much larger than ourselves.

Regardless of our age or background, nature journaling offers a path to inner peace that is accessible to everyone. Whether you are a seasoned artist or a novice with a pencil, all that is required is an open heart and a willingness to connect with the beauty of the natural world. So grab your journal, find a peaceful spot in nature, and allow the healing touch of Earth to guide you on a journey of reflection and self-discovery.

Chapter 4: Overcoming Challenges in Nature Meditation

Dealing with Distractions

In the fast-paced world we live in today, distractions seem to be everywhere. From the constant pinging of our smartphones to the never-ending stream of notifications, it can be challenging to find a moment of peace and inner calm. However, amidst the chaos of our daily lives, nature offers a sanctuary where we can find solace and regain our focus. In this subchapter, we will explore effective strategies for dealing with distractions and harnessing the peace of nature to find inner peace.

1. Disconnect to Reconnect: One of the most powerful ways to deal with distractions is to disconnect from technology and reconnect with nature. Take a break from the digital world and immerse yourself in the beauty of the natural world. Engage your senses by feeling the earth beneath your feet, listening to the soothing sounds of birds chirping, and breathing in the fresh air. This mindful connection with nature can help you let go of distractions and find a sense of inner peace.

2. Practice Mindfulness: Mindfulness is a powerful tool for dealing with distractions. By cultivating a non-judgmental awareness of the present moment, you can train your mind to focus on what truly matters. When distractions arise, acknowledge them without judgment and gently bring your attention back to the present moment. Engage all your senses in the experience of nature, noticing the intricate details of a flower or the gentle rustling of leaves. This

practice will help you develop resilience against distractions and find peace in the simplicity of the natural world.

3. Create a Routine: Establishing a routine can also help you deal with distractions. Set aside dedicated time each day to immerse yourself in nature, whether it's a morning walk in the park or an evening meditation by the beach. By making nature a regular part of your life, you create a space for tranquility and focus, away from the chaos of distractions.

4. Embrace Nature's Lessons: Nature often teaches us important lessons about resilience and adaptability. Observe the way plants and animals cope with external challenges, and apply those lessons to your own life. Just as a tree bends with the wind but remains grounded, learn to adapt to distractions without losing your inner peace. Embrace the stillness and wisdom of nature, allowing it to guide you through the storm of distractions.

By implementing these strategies, you can navigate the overwhelming distractions of modern life and find solace in the peace of nature. Remember, the natural world offers a constant source of healing and tranquility; all we need to do is open our hearts and embrace its gentle touch.

Acknowledging and accepting distractions during meditation

In the serene realm of meditation, it is common for distractions to arise. These distractions can come in various forms, from the external noise of the world to the internal chatter of our minds. However, instead of viewing these distractions as obstacles to our practice, we can learn to acknowledge and accept them as part of the journey towards inner peace and harmony.

Meditation is a powerful tool that allows us to connect with our inner selves and find solace in the present moment. By immersing ourselves in the beauty of nature, we can enhance the transformative experience of meditation. The peace of nature has a unique ability to calm our minds, allowing us to detach from the chaos of daily life and find solace in the simplicity and stillness of the natural world.

During meditation, it is essential to acknowledge the distractions that may arise. Whether it is the sound of birds chirping, the rustling of leaves, or our own thoughts clamoring for attention, we must recognize these distractions without judgment. Instead of trying to push them away or suppress them, we can learn to accept their presence and gently redirect our focus back to our breath or chosen point of concentration.

By acknowledging distractions, we cultivate a sense of mindfulness that allows us to observe them without becoming entangled in their grip. We can view distractions as opportunities for growth, as they provide valuable insights into the workings of our minds. Through practicing acceptance, we learn to let go of the need for control and surrender to the flow of our thoughts and emotions.

The peace of nature serves as a gentle reminder that distractions are a natural part of life. Just as the wind blows through the trees or a river flows effortlessly, distractions come and go. By embracing this truth, we free ourselves from frustration and cultivate a sense of peace within ourselves.

In the pursuit of inner peace, it is essential to remember that distractions do not define our meditation practice. Instead, they offer us a chance to deepen our awareness and strengthen our ability to remain present. By acknowledging and accepting distractions during meditation, we embark on a transformative journey towards finding inner peace in the natural world.

In conclusion, the subchapter "Acknowledging and Accepting Distractions during Meditation" emphasizes the importance of embracing distractions as part of the meditation process. By immersing ourselves in the peace of nature, we can find solace and enhance our practice. Through acceptance and mindfulness, we free ourselves from frustration and deepen our connection with the present moment. Ultimately, by acknowledging and accepting distractions, we embark on a transformative journey towards finding inner peace in the natural world.

Techniques for refocusing your attention in nature

In today's fast-paced and technology-driven world, finding inner peace can often feel like an elusive goal. However, one need not look further than the natural world to discover its incredible healing touch. Nature has a way of grounding us and helping us reconnect with ourselves and the present moment. By refocusing our attention in nature, we can find solace, tranquility, and a renewed sense of inner peace.

Here are some techniques that can help you refocus your attention and find peace in the embrace of nature:

1. Mindful walking: Take a slow, deliberate walk in nature, paying attention to every step and the sensations you experience. Notice the texture of the ground beneath your feet, the rustling of leaves, and the scents in the air. By fully immersing yourself in the present moment, you can quiet the chatter of your mind and find inner stillness.

2. Sensory exploration: Engage all your senses while spending time in nature. Feel the cool breeze on your skin, listen to the soothing sounds of birds chirping or water flowing, and inhale the earthy aroma of the forest. By awakening your senses, you can fully experience the beauty and peace that nature offers.

3. Nature journaling: Bring a journal with you on your nature walks and take the time to observe and document what you see. Describe the colors, shapes, and patterns of flowers, trees, and wildlife. Write down any thoughts or emotions that arise during your experience. Nature journaling can help you deepen your connection with nature and reflect on the profound impact it has on your inner well-being.

4. Meditative sitting: Find a quiet spot in nature where you can sit comfortably. Close your eyes and focus on your breath, allowing yourself to fully relax and let go of any tension or stress. As you sit in stillness, let the sounds, smells, and sensations of nature wash over you. This meditation practice can help you cultivate a deep sense of peace and connection with the natural world.

5. Immersion in water: Whether it's taking a dip in a nearby lake or soaking your feet in a bubbling stream, water has a unique ability to calm and rejuvenate. Allow yourself to fully immerse in the experience, feeling the water's gentle touch and letting it wash away any worries or negative emotions.

By practicing these techniques for refocusing your attention in nature, you can tap into the incredible healing power of the natural world. As you find peace in nature, you will discover a profound sense of inner calm, rejuvenation, and connection with yourself and the world around you. Embrace the healing touch of Earth and allow it to guide you on your journey towards inner peace.

Developing resilience in the face of distractions

In today's fast-paced world, distractions seem to be everywhere. From the constant notifications on our phones to the never-ending stream of information bombarding us from all directions, it's becoming increasingly difficult to find a moment of peace and tranquility. However, amidst the chaos, there is a powerful tool that can help us cultivate resilience and find inner peace – the healing touch of nature.

The subchapter "Developing Resilience in the Face of Distractions" from the book "Earth's Healing Touch: Mindful Practices for Finding Inner Peace in the Natural World" aims to guide every individual, regardless of their background or interests, towards rediscovering the soothing power of nature and using it as a source of strength and resilience.

Nature has a way of grounding us, bringing us back to our true selves and reminding us of the beauty and simplicity that exists beyond the distractions of modern life. When we immerse ourselves in the peace of nature, we can tap into a wellspring of resilience that helps us navigate the challenges and distractions that come our way.

This subchapter offers practical tips and mindful practices that anyone can incorporate into their daily lives. It explores the benefits of spending time in nature, such as reduced stress levels, improved mental clarity, and increased overall well-being. It also delves into the science behind nature's healing touch, explaining how exposure to natural environments can positively impact our brain chemistry and emotional state.

Readers will discover a range of techniques for developing resilience in the face of distractions. These may include mindfulness exercises that can be practiced amidst the beauty of a natural setting, such as grounding exercises, deep breathing techniques, and sensory awareness practices. The subchapter also encourages individuals to disconnect from technology and reconnect with the natural world, offering suggestions for digital detoxes and ways to create tech-free zones in their daily lives.

Ultimately, the goal of "Developing Resilience in the Face of Distractions" is to empower readers to find solace and strength in the peace of nature. By embracing the healing touch of the natural world, individuals can cultivate resilience, enhance their well-being, and find inner peace amidst the chaos of modern life. This subchapter seeks to remind every individual of the transformative power of nature and the importance of prioritizing moments of tranquility in their busy lives.

Weather and Environmental Factors

The natural world has always held a unique and powerful ability to bring us peace and tranquility. Whether it's the serene sound of raindrops falling, the gentle warmth of the sun on our skin, or the cool, crisp air that fills our lungs, nature has a healing touch that can help us find inner peace. In this subchapter, we will explore the various weather and environmental factors that contribute to our sense of peace in the natural world.

One of the most captivating aspects of nature is its ability to constantly change and adapt. The weather plays a significant role in this, providing a dynamic backdrop for our experiences in the great outdoors. From the calm and serene days to the stormy and turbulent ones, each weather condition offers its own unique opportunities for finding peace. The sound of rain falling can be incredibly soothing, creating a sense of calm and tranquility. The rhythmic patter of raindrops on leaves or the roof of a shelter can lull us into a state of peacefulness, allowing our minds to wander and our stress to melt away.

On the other hand, the warmth of the sun can have a rejuvenating effect on our bodies and minds. Basking in the sun's rays can provide a sense of comfort and relaxation, allowing us to connect with the natural world around us. The gentle warmth can ease tension in our muscles and release endorphins, promoting a sense of well-being and peace.

Environmental factors also play a significant role in our peace of nature. The sights, sounds, and smells of the natural world can all contribute to our sense of tranquility. The vibrant colors of flowers in bloom or the majestic sight of a waterfall can captivate our senses and bring us a deep sense of peace. The sounds of birds chirping or the rustling of leaves in the wind can be incredibly soothing, creating a harmonious symphony that resonates with our souls. Even the scent of fresh pine or the salty ocean air can transport us to a place of serenity and calm.

By understanding and appreciating the various weather and environmental factors that contribute to our peace of nature, we can fully immerse ourselves in the healing power of the natural world. Whether it's the gentle rain, the warm sun, or the sights and sounds of the environment, nature has a way of providing us with inner peace and a sense of connection to something greater than ourselves. So, venture outside, embrace the weather, and allow the healing touch of nature to bring you the peace you seek.

Adapting to different weather conditions

In our modern-day lives, we are often shielded from the whims of the weather. We have air-conditioned homes, heated cars, and umbrellas to protect us from rain. However, by disconnecting ourselves from the natural world, we miss out on the valuable lessons it can teach us. Adapting to different weather conditions is not only essential for survival but also offers an opportunity to find inner peace in the natural world.

Nature is a powerful teacher, and one of its most profound lessons is adaptability. Just as animals and plants have learned to adapt to various climates and weather patterns, we too can learn from their wisdom. Whether it is a scorching hot day or a freezing winter night, there are valuable lessons to be learned from the weather.

One of the first lessons we can learn from adapting to different weather conditions is the importance of being present. When it is pouring rain, it is difficult to focus on anything else but the sensation of the raindrops on our skin. In those moments, we become fully present in the here and now, experiencing the natural world in all its glory. This sense of presence can bring us peace and tranquility, allowing us to let go of our worries and find solace in the beauty of the rain.

Moreover, adapting to different weather conditions can teach us resilience. Nature is resilient; it withstands storms, droughts, and extreme temperatures. By observing nature's resilience, we can learn to embrace change and face challenges with grace and determination.

Just as a tree bends with the wind, we too can adapt and find strength in the face of adversity.

Furthermore, adapting to different weather conditions can foster a deep connection with the natural world. When we take the time to understand the patterns and rhythms of the weather, we become more attuned to the earth's energy. We begin to appreciate the delicate balance of nature and realize our interconnectedness with all living beings. This connection brings a sense of peace and harmony, as we recognize that we are part of something much larger than ourselves.

In conclusion, adapting to different weather conditions is not just a practical skill, but an opportunity for personal growth and inner peace. Through presence, resilience, and connection, we can learn valuable lessons from the natural world that can guide us in finding harmony within ourselves. So, the next time you find yourself caught in a rainstorm or basking in the warmth of the sun, take a moment to embrace the weather and let it teach you its wisdom.

Utilizing nature's elements to enhance your meditation

In our fast-paced, technology-driven society, finding inner peace can often seem like an elusive quest. However, the answers we seek may be closer than we think – right in the embrace of nature's elements. The serenity and tranquility found in the natural world can provide the perfect backdrop for enhancing our meditation practices. In this subchapter, we will explore how you can harness the power of nature to deepen your connection with yourself and find inner peace.

One of the most fundamental elements of nature is the air we breathe. As you embark on your meditation journey, take a moment to focus on your breath. Feel the coolness as you inhale and the warmth as you exhale. Observe how the air enters and leaves your body, allowing it to cleanse and rejuvenate your mind, body, and spirit. Let it remind you of the vastness and interconnectedness of the world around you.

Another powerful element is water. Whether it's a babbling brook, a serene lake, or the crashing waves of the ocean, water has an innate ability to calm our senses. Incorporate water into your meditation by finding a peaceful spot near a water source. Close your eyes and listen to the soothing sounds as the water flows effortlessly. Imagine yourself being cleansed and purified, just like the water, as you let go of any stress or negativity.

Earth, the very ground beneath our feet, offers stability and grounding. Find a comfortable spot outdoors and connect with the earth's energy. As you sit or lie down, feel the support of the earth beneath you. Visualize roots extending from your body into the ground, anchoring you to the present moment. Allow the earth's energy to flow through you, grounding and centering your mind.

Lastly, fire represents transformation and renewal. Incorporate the element of fire into your meditation by lighting a candle or sitting by a bonfire. As you observe the flickering flames, let them symbolize the burning away of any negative thoughts or emotions. Feel the warmth and energy radiating from the fire, igniting a sense of passion and purpose within you.

In conclusion, nature's elements offer a multitude of opportunities to enhance your meditation practice. By consciously connecting with the air, water, earth, and fire, you can deepen your sense of inner peace and find solace in the natural world. Embrace the healing touch of nature and allow its elements to guide you on your journey towards self-discovery and serenity. Remember, nature is always there, patiently waiting to offer its wisdom and support to everyone seeking peace.

Finding inner peace regardless of external circumstances

In a fast-paced and chaotic world, finding inner peace seems like an elusive goal. We often believe that external circumstances dictate our emotions and state of mind. However, the truth is that regardless of what is happening around us, we have the power to cultivate inner peace. This subchapter aims to guide every individual, particularly those seeking peace in the embrace of nature, on the journey towards finding serenity within themselves.

Nature has a profound ability to heal and restore our inner balance. When we immerse ourselves in the peacefulness of natural surroundings, we can tap into the inherent tranquility that exists within us. The rustling of leaves, the gentle flow of a river, or the melodious chirping of birds can all serve as reminders to slow down, breathe, and connect with our inner selves.

One key aspect of finding inner peace regardless of external circumstances is practicing mindfulness. By being fully present in the moment, we can detach ourselves from the chaos and stress that often consumes our daily lives. Mindfulness allows us to observe our thoughts and emotions without judgment, giving us the freedom to choose how we respond to external circumstances. In the serenity of nature, mindfulness becomes easier to embrace as we become attuned to the rhythm of life around us.

Another powerful tool in finding inner peace is gratitude. When we cultivate a deep sense of appreciation for the beauty and wonder of the natural world, we shift our focus from what is lacking in our lives to what is abundant. Gratitude helps us reframe our perspective, reminding us of the blessings that surround us even in the face of adversity.

Moreover, connecting with nature can ignite a sense of awe and wonder within us. As we witness the intricate ecosystems, the power of the elements, and the cycle of life and death, we are reminded of our own place in the grand tapestry of existence. This profound connection fosters humility, acceptance, and a deep sense of peace.

Ultimately, finding inner peace regardless of external circumstances is a lifelong journey that requires intention, practice, and patience. By immersing ourselves in the peace of nature, practicing mindfulness, cultivating gratitude, and embracing awe, we can tap into our innate ability to find serenity within ourselves, no matter what challenges life presents us. The natural world serves as our guide, offering solace, inspiration, and a gentle reminder that peace is always within reach.

Integrating Nature Meditation into Daily Life

In our modern, fast-paced world, finding inner peace and tranquility can often feel like an impossible task. We are constantly bombarded with stressors, distractions, and the demands of daily life. However, there is a simple yet powerful practice that can help us reconnect with ourselves and find peace amidst the chaos - nature meditation.

Nature meditation is a practice that involves immersing oneself in the natural world and using it as a focal point for meditation. By engaging our senses and stilling our minds, we can tap into the healing power of nature and experience a profound sense of peace and connection.

One of the greatest benefits of nature meditation is its accessibility. It can be practiced by anyone, regardless of age, background, or physical ability. All you need is a quiet spot outdoors, whether it's a nearby park, a garden, or even your own backyard. Find a comfortable position, close your eyes, and take a deep breath, allowing yourself to fully arrive in the present moment.

Begin by anchoring your attention to the sounds around you. Listen to the birds singing, the rustling of leaves, or the gentle flow of a nearby stream. Let these sounds become the backdrop for your meditation, allowing them to guide you deeper into a state of relaxation and calm.

As you continue your practice, shift your focus to the sensations in your body. Feel the warmth of the sun on your skin, the coolness of the breeze against your face, or the texture of the earth beneath your feet. Allow these sensations to ground you and bring you into a state of embodied presence.

Next, open your eyes and let your gaze rest on a natural object or scene that captures your attention. It could be a flower, a tree, or a body of water. Take in its beauty and let it fill you with a sense of awe and wonder. Notice the intricate details, the colors, and the patterns. Allow yourself to be fully present with this moment of connection.

As you conclude your meditation, take a few moments to express gratitude for the healing power of nature. Acknowledge the peace and tranquility it has brought into your life, and carry this sense of connection and gratitude with you as you go about your day.

Integrating nature meditation into daily life is a transformative practice that can bring immense peace and joy. By taking the time to connect with the natural world, even for just a few minutes each day, we can find solace, grounding, and a renewed sense of inner peace. So, step outside, embrace the beauty of nature, and allow it to be your guide on the path to peace.

Incorporating mindfulness practices in your daily routine

In today's fast-paced and hectic world, finding inner peace and tranquility can seem like an elusive goal. However, there is a simple yet powerful solution that can help you achieve a sense of calm and balance – mindfulness. By incorporating mindfulness practices into your daily routine, you can tap into the healing power of nature and experience profound inner peace.

Mindfulness is the practice of being fully present in the moment, without judgment or attachment. It is about cultivating awareness of your thoughts, feelings, and sensations as they arise, and learning to respond to them with kindness and compassion. By practicing mindfulness, you can bring a sense of peace, clarity, and harmony into your life.

One of the most effective ways to incorporate mindfulness into your daily routine is by connecting with the peace of nature. The natural world has a unique ability to soothe our minds, uplift our spirits, and restore our sense of well-being. By immersing ourselves in nature and mindfully engaging with its wonders, we can tap into its healing touch and find inner peace.

Start by setting aside some time each day to be in nature. It could be as simple as taking a walk in a nearby park or sitting in your backyard, surrounded by nature's beauty. As you step into the peaceful embrace of nature, allow yourself to fully experience the sights, sounds, and sensations around you. Take deep breaths, noticing the scents of flowers or the crispness of the air. Tune into the symphony of birdsong or the gentle rustling of leaves. Feel the earth beneath your feet and the warmth of the sun on your skin.

As you connect with nature, bring your attention to the present moment. Notice any thoughts or worries that arise, but gently let them go, allowing yourself to be fully present in the here and now. Feel a sense of gratitude for the beauty and abundance of the natural world, and let it fill your heart with peace and joy.

In addition to being in nature, you can also incorporate mindfulness practices throughout your day. Practice mindful eating by savoring each bite of your meals, paying attention to the flavors, textures, and nourishment they provide. Engage in mindful movement by practicing yoga or tai chi, allowing your body to move with grace and ease. Cultivate mindful relationships by truly listening to others and being fully present in your interactions.

By incorporating mindfulness practices into your daily routine, you can harness the power of nature to find inner peace and tranquility. Remember, mindfulness is not just a practice; it is a way of life. Embrace the beauty of the natural world and let it guide you on your journey to finding inner peace and harmony.

Bringing nature's healing touch into your home and workspace

In the hustle and bustle of our daily lives, it is easy to become disconnected from the natural world around us. We spend hours indoors, surrounded by walls and artificial lights, unaware of the healing power that nature holds. But what if we could bring nature's calming and rejuvenating influence into our own homes and workspaces? In this subchapter, we will explore the ways in which you can invite the peace of nature into your life, regardless of where you are.

Creating an environment that reflects the beauty of nature can have a profound impact on our overall well-being. Consider incorporating natural elements such as plants, stones, or water features into your living and working spaces. Not only do they add a touch of serenity, but they also purify the air and improve our physical health. Surrounding ourselves with greenery and natural materials can evoke a sense of tranquility and connection to the earth.

Engaging our senses is another powerful way to bring nature's healing touch indoors. Fill your space with scents that remind you of the outdoors, such as essential oils or fresh flowers. Play soft nature sounds or use a white noise machine that mimics the sound of a gentle rain shower. These sensory experiences can transport us to a peaceful state of mind, even when we are stuck inside.

In addition to transforming our physical surroundings, we can also integrate mindfulness practices inspired by nature into our daily routines. Take a few moments each day to observe the beauty of a sunrise or sunset, even if it's just from your window. Practice grounding techniques that involve connecting with the earth, such as walking barefoot on grass or sand. These simple acts can help us feel more connected to the natural world and cultivate a sense of inner peace.

Remember, you don't have to venture far to experience the healing touch of nature. By intentionally creating a space that reflects the peace of nature, incorporating sensory experiences, and practicing mindfulness, you can bring the essence of the outdoors into your home and workspace. Embrace the restorative power of nature and discover the transformative effects it can have on your well-being.

Nurturing a sustainable lifestyle through mindfulness in nature

Nurturing a sustainable lifestyle through mindfulness in nature is a subchapter in the book "Earth's Healing Touch: Mindful Practices for Finding Inner Peace in the Natural World" that aims to inspire and guide individuals from all walks of life towards embracing a more sustainable lifestyle through the practice of mindfulness in nature.

In today's fast-paced and technology-driven world, many individuals find themselves disconnected from the natural world. However, research has shown that spending time in nature can have profound positive effects on our mental, emotional, and physical well-being. By becoming mindful of our surroundings and cultivating a deep connection with nature, we can not only find inner peace but also contribute to the preservation and sustainability of our planet.

The subchapter begins by emphasizing the importance of reconnecting with nature and its healing powers. It encourages readers to step away from their busy lives and immerse themselves in the tranquility and beauty of the natural world. By doing so, individuals can experience a sense of peace, calmness, and rejuvenation.

The chapter then delves into various mindful practices that can be incorporated into everyday life to nurture a sustainable lifestyle. It introduces the concept of mindfulness, which involves paying attention to the present moment without judgment. By applying mindfulness to our interactions with nature, we can develop a deep appreciation for its wonders and become more conscious of our impact on the environment.

The subchapter explores practices such as mindful walking, where individuals focus on the sensations of each step and fully engage their senses in the natural surroundings. It also suggests mindful gardening, which involves cultivating a garden with love and care, honoring the natural cycles of growth and decay.

Furthermore, the chapter addresses the importance of consuming consciously and sustainably. It encourages readers to make mindful choices when purchasing food, clothing, and other products, considering their environmental impact. By adopting practices such as reducing waste, recycling, and supporting local and organic producers, individuals can contribute to a more sustainable world.

Overall, the subchapter "Nurturing a sustainable lifestyle through mindfulness in nature" emphasizes the power of mindfulness in fostering a deep connection with the natural world. It highlights the importance of embracing sustainable practices and offers practical suggestions to incorporate mindfulness into everyday life. By doing so, readers can find inner peace and become agents of positive change, contributing to the well-being of both themselves and the planet we call home.

Chapter 5: Deepening the Connection with Nature

Environmental Stewardship and Conservation

In today's fast-paced world, finding peace and tranquility can be a challenge. However, one surefire way to reconnect with ourselves and find inner peace is by immersing ourselves in the beauty of nature. The subchapter on Environmental Stewardship and Conservation in "Earth's Healing Touch: Mindful Practices for Finding Inner Peace in the Natural World" aims to inspire and guide individuals from all walks of life towards embracing the peace that nature offers and becoming responsible stewards of the environment.

Nature has a unique ability to soothe our souls and restore our inner balance. Whether it's the gentle rustling of leaves in a forest, the melodious chirping of birds in the early morning, or the rhythmic crashing of waves on a beach, nature's symphony has a profound impact on our overall well-being. By engaging in mindful practices and being present in nature, we can cultivate a deep sense of peace and connection with the world around us.

However, it is not enough to simply enjoy the peace that nature brings. As individuals who benefit from the healing touch of the natural world, it is our duty to become mindful stewards and conservationists. Environmental stewardship involves recognizing the interconnectedness of all living beings and taking actions that promote the well-being of the planet.

This subchapter provides practical insights and tips on how to become better environmental stewards. It explores topics such as reducing our carbon footprint, conserving water and energy, practicing sustainable living, and supporting local ecosystems. It also delves into the importance of protecting endangered species, preserving biodiversity, and advocating for environmental policies.

By actively participating in environmental stewardship and conservation efforts, we not only contribute to the preservation of our planet but also deepen our connection with nature. Taking small steps, such as recycling, using eco-friendly products, and participating in community clean-up events, can have a significant impact on the environment and our personal sense of fulfillment.

"Earth's Healing Touch: Mindful Practices for Finding Inner Peace in the Natural World" encourages every individual to embrace the peace of nature and become environmental stewards. It emphasizes that by caring for the planet, we are ultimately caring for ourselves. Through our collective actions, we can create a world where peace and harmony with nature thrive for generations to come. Let us embark on this journey together and make a positive difference in our own lives and the world around us.

Understanding the interconnectedness of all living beings

In our fast-paced, modern world, it is easy to lose sight of the deep connections that exist between all living beings. We often find ourselves disconnected from nature, consumed by our own individual lives and concerns. However, it is crucial to recognize and appreciate the interconnectedness of all living beings, as it is through this understanding that we can find true peace and harmony in both ourselves and the natural world.

One of the fundamental principles of ecology is the concept of interconnectedness. Every living being, from the tiniest insect to the largest tree, plays a vital role in maintaining the delicate balance of our planet. Each organism is intricately linked to one another, forming a complex web of relationships that sustains life. When we begin to grasp the depth and significance of these connections, we can then appreciate the peace that nature offers.

Nature provides us with a profound sense of calm and tranquility. From the soothing sound of a babbling brook to the gentle rustling of leaves in the wind, the natural world has a unique ability to quiet our minds and restore our souls. When we immerse ourselves in the peace of nature, we become acutely aware of our place within the greater tapestry of life. We begin to understand that our actions have consequences that ripple through the interconnected web of existence.

Recognizing our interconnectedness with all living beings also fosters a sense of empathy and compassion. When we realize that the suffering or destruction of one species affects us all, we are motivated to take action and protect our environment. This understanding prompts us to live more mindfully, making choices that are in alignment with the well-being of the planet and its inhabitants.

In this chapter, we will explore various practices and techniques that can deepen our understanding of the interconnectedness of all living beings. We will learn to develop a sense of gratitude for the natural world, finding solace and inner peace through mindful engagement with our environment. By cultivating a deep connection with nature, we can begin to heal ourselves and contribute to the healing of the Earth.

Whether you are a nature enthusiast, a seeker of inner peace, or someone who simply appreciates the beauty of the world around you, this chapter will provide you with valuable insights and practical tools for understanding and embracing the interconnectedness of all living beings. Through the wisdom of nature, we can find the peace we seek, both within ourselves and in the world. Let us embark on this journey together, as we rediscover our place within the intricate tapestry of life.

Taking action to protect and preserve the natural environment

Taking action to protect and preserve the natural environment is essential for our collective well-being and the future of our planet. In today's fast-paced world, where technology dominates our lives, it is crucial to reconnect with nature and understand the significance of its preservation. Earth's Healing Touch: Mindful Practices for Finding Inner Peace in the Natural World serves as a guidebook to inspire every individual, regardless of their background or interests, to take steps towards protecting and preserving the natural environment.

In this subchapter, we delve into the various ways we can actively contribute to the conservation of our natural world. It begins by emphasizing the importance of mindfulness in our daily lives. By cultivating a sense of mindfulness, we become aware of the impact of our actions on the environment. We learn to appreciate the beauty and serenity of nature, fostering a deep connection that motivates us to protect it.

The subchapter then explores practical actions that individuals can take to make a difference. It encourages readers to reduce their carbon footprint by adopting sustainable practices, such as conserving energy, using public transportation, or embracing renewable energy sources. Additionally, it highlights the significance of waste reduction and recycling in minimizing our impact on the environment.

Readers are also encouraged to support local organic farmers and engage in sustainable food practices. By choosing organic produce and reducing meat consumption, we can promote biodiversity and reduce the environmental strain caused by intensive agriculture.

Furthermore, the subchapter emphasizes the importance of preserving and restoring natural habitats. It discusses the significance of participating in local conservation projects, volunteering in wildlife rehabilitation centers, or donating to organizations dedicated to protecting endangered species.

The content also explores the role of advocacy and political engagement in protecting the natural environment. It encourages readers to participate in environmental campaigns, sign petitions, and contact their representatives to push for stronger environmental policies.

Ultimately, this subchapter aims to inspire every individual to take immediate action to protect and preserve the natural environment. By promoting awareness, education, and practical steps, Earth's Healing Touch provides a roadmap for achieving inner peace through our connection with nature, while also safeguarding the planet for future generations. Let us all come together and embrace the peace of nature, taking action to heal our earth and find inner peace in the process.

Contributing to sustainable practices for future generations

In this fast-paced and ever-changing world, it is crucial for each and every one of us to take responsibility for our actions and contribute to sustainable practices for the well-being of future generations. As lovers of peace and nature, we have a unique role to play in preserving the natural world and ensuring its healing touch remains accessible to all.

Sustainability is about finding a delicate balance between meeting our present needs without compromising the ability of future generations to meet their own. It encompasses various aspects, including environmental, social, and economic considerations. By embracing sustainable practices, we can create a harmonious relationship with nature and foster a more peaceful world.

One of the first steps towards contributing to sustainability is to educate ourselves about the impact of our daily choices. From the food we eat to the products we consume, each decision we make has far-reaching consequences for the environment. By opting for organic and locally sourced food, reducing our energy consumption, and supporting eco-friendly businesses, we can significantly reduce our ecological footprint.

Another important aspect of sustainability is preserving biodiversity and protecting natural habitats. By supporting conservation organizations, volunteering for environmental projects, or even participating in reforestation efforts, we can actively contribute to the preservation of our planet's invaluable ecosystems. By doing so, we ensure that future generations can continue to experience the healing power of nature firsthand.

Furthermore, sustainable practices also extend to our social interactions and economic systems. By promoting fair trade, supporting ethical businesses, and advocating for social justice, we can create a more equitable and sustainable society. This includes empowering marginalized communities, advocating for human rights, and reducing inequality. After all, peace cannot exist without justice.

Ultimately, contributing to sustainable practices for future generations is not just a responsibility but also an opportunity for personal growth and fulfillment. By embracing a mindful approach to our actions and cultivating a deep connection with nature, we can find inner peace and harmony. Our relationship with the natural world is a reflection of our inner selves, and by nurturing it, we can create a ripple effect of positive change in the world.

In conclusion, as lovers of peace and nature, we have a unique role to play in contributing to sustainable practices for future generations. By educating ourselves, preserving biodiversity, supporting ethical practices, and advocating for social justice, we can create a more harmonious and sustainable world. Let us embrace the healing touch of the earth and be mindful of our actions, ensuring a brighter and more peaceful future for all.

Ecopsychology and the Healing Power of Nature

In today's fast-paced and technology-driven world, it is easy to feel disconnected from ourselves and the natural world around us. We often find ourselves overwhelmed with stress, anxiety, and a constant sense of restlessness. However, there is a simple, yet profound solution to finding inner peace – the healing power of nature.

Ecopsychology is a field that explores the relationship between humans and the natural environment, emphasizing the interconnectedness and interdependence of all living beings. It recognizes that our well-being is deeply intertwined with the health and vitality of the Earth. Through this lens, we can begin to understand how spending time in nature can have a profound healing effect on our minds, bodies, and souls.

Nature has a way of captivating us and bringing us into the present moment. Whether it's the vibrant colors of a sunset, the soothing sound of waves crashing on the shore, or the gentle touch of a cool breeze on our skin, nature has a way of awakening our senses and grounding us in the here and now. As we immerse ourselves in the peace of nature, we begin to let go of our worries and anxieties, finding solace in the simplicity and beauty that surrounds us.

Studies have shown that spending time in nature can have a positive impact on our mental health. It reduces stress, anxiety, and depression, while increasing feelings of happiness, calmness, and overall well-being. Nature acts as a natural antidepressant, boosting our mood and improving our cognitive function. It allows us to slow down, breathe deeply, and find a sense of inner peace that is often elusive in our daily lives.

Moreover, connecting with nature can also be a powerful tool for self-discovery and personal growth. As we observe the cycles of nature – the changing seasons, the ebb and flow of tides, and the constant renewal of life – we are reminded of the impermanence and interconnectedness of all things. We begin to see ourselves as part of a larger web of life, and our problems and worries begin to feel less significant in the grand scheme of things.

Whether it's hiking through a lush forest, strolling along a sandy beach, or simply sitting under a tree in a local park, finding peace in nature is accessible to everyone. It is a gentle and nurturing reminder of our inherent connection to the Earth, offering us solace, healing, and a renewed sense of purpose. So, take a moment to step outside, breathe in the fresh air, and let the healing power of nature wash over you, bringing you back to a state of inner peace and harmony.

Exploring the psychological benefits of nature immersion

In today's fast-paced and technology-driven world, finding inner peace can often feel like an elusive goal. However, one of the most effective ways to reconnect with ourselves and experience a sense of tranquility is by immersing ourselves in nature. This subchapter will delve into the profound psychological benefits of nature immersion, and how it can bring us closer to finding inner peace.

Nature has a unique power to heal and restore our mental well-being. When we spend time surrounded by the beauty of the natural world, our senses awaken, and our minds begin to quiet. The peace and serenity offered by nature provide a much-needed respite from the constant noise and stimulation of modern life.

One of the primary psychological benefits of nature immersion is its ability to reduce stress and anxiety. Research has shown that spending time in natural environments can lower our heart rate, blood pressure, and cortisol levels. The soothing sounds of birds chirping, the gentle rustling of leaves, and the scent of fresh air all work together to create a calming effect on our nervous system.

Furthermore, nature immersion can improve our mood and increase feelings of happiness. Being outdoors exposes us to natural sunlight, which boosts our vitamin D levels and enhances our overall well-being. Additionally, the vibrant colors and textures found in nature have a positive impact on our emotional state, promoting feelings of joy and contentment.

Another psychological benefit of nature immersion is its ability to enhance our creativity and problem-solving skills. Being in a natural environment stimulates our senses and encourages us to think more freely and expansively. Studies have shown that spending time in nature can improve cognitive function, increase focus, and enhance our ability to generate new ideas.

In addition to these benefits, nature immersion fosters a sense of connection and belonging. When we immerse ourselves in the natural world, we become aware of our interconnectedness with all living beings. This awareness can lead to a greater sense of empathy, compassion, and a deeper appreciation for the beauty and diversity of life.

In conclusion, exploring and immersing ourselves in nature offers a multitude of psychological benefits. From reducing stress and anxiety to enhancing creativity and promoting a sense of connection, nature has a profound impact on our mental well-being. By prioritizing time in nature and practicing mindful engagement with the natural world, we can discover the healing touch of Earth and find inner peace within ourselves. So, step outside, breathe in the fresh air, and allow nature to guide you on a journey towards tranquility and inner harmony.

Healing trauma and promoting mental well-being through ecotherapy

In today's fast-paced, technology-driven world, many of us find ourselves yearning for a sense of peace and tranquility. We seek solace in the beauty of nature, yearning to reconnect with the natural world that once nurtured and sustained us. It is in this pursuit of inner peace that ecotherapy, also known as nature therapy, has emerged as a powerful tool for healing trauma and promoting mental well-being.

Ecotherapy recognizes the profound impact that nature has on our mental and emotional well-being. It is a holistic approach that combines the healing power of nature with mindful practices to restore balance and harmony within ourselves. In the book "Earth's Healing Touch: Mindful Practices for Finding Inner Peace in the Natural World," we explore the transformative potential of ecotherapy and how it can benefit each and every one of us.

Trauma, whether caused by a single event or prolonged exposure to stress, can have a lasting impact on our mental health. Ecotherapy offers a unique and gentle way to address these wounds by reconnecting us with the healing energy of the natural world. By immersing ourselves in nature, we can find respite from the chaos of our daily lives and create a safe space for healing to occur.

Through ecotherapy, we learn to engage our senses and be fully present in the natural environment. We practice mindfulness, allowing ourselves to observe and appreciate the beauty and serenity that surrounds us. This mindful connection with nature has been shown to reduce anxiety, alleviate symptoms of depression, and improve overall well-being.

In "Earth's Healing Touch," we delve into various ecotherapy techniques that harness the power of nature to heal trauma and promote mental well-being. From forest bathing to nature journaling, we provide practical exercises that can be easily incorporated into your daily life. We also explore the science behind ecotherapy, revealing the physiological and psychological benefits of spending time in nature.

Whether you are seeking peace of mind, relief from stress, or healing from trauma, "Earth's Healing Touch" offers a roadmap to finding inner peace in the natural world. By embracing ecotherapy, you can tap into the restorative power of nature and discover a profound sense of well-being that can transform your life.

Join us on this journey to harness the peace of nature and unlock the healing potential that lies within our natural surroundings. Let "Earth's Healing Touch" be your guide to finding inner peace, one mindful step at a time.

Embracing nature as a source of spiritual nourishment

In our fast-paced and technology-driven world, it's easy to become disconnected from the natural world around us. We often find ourselves caught up in the chaos of our daily lives, constantly bombarded with to-do lists and the demands of modern society. However, deep within each of us lies a yearning for peace and tranquility.

Nature has long been recognized as a powerful source of healing and spiritual nourishment. From the towering mountains to the gentle flow of a river, the natural world offers us a sanctuary to find solace, rejuvenate our spirits, and reconnect with our inner selves.

In the subchapter "Embracing Nature as a Source of Spiritual Nourishment," we explore the profound impact that immersing ourselves in the peace of nature can have on our well-being. Whether you're a seasoned nature lover or just beginning to discover its wonders, this chapter is for everyone seeking a deeper connection with themselves and the world around them.

We delve into various mindful practices that can guide you on this transformative journey. From mindful walking in the forest to meditating by the ocean, we explore the different ways in which nature can become a powerful teacher and healer. We'll also discuss the importance of being present in the moment and how it allows us to fully embrace the nourishing qualities of nature.

Moreover, we'll delve into the science behind the healing power of nature. Discover how spending time in natural environments can lower stress levels, boost our immune system, and improve our mental health. Through studies and personal anecdotes, we'll shed light on the amazing benefits that nature has to offer.

Through this subchapter, we hope to inspire you to pause, breathe, and fully immerse yourself in the peace of nature. We invite you to explore the hidden gems that surround us, whether it's a nearby park, a quiet garden, or a distant mountain range. By embracing nature as a source of spiritual nourishment, we can find inner peace, cultivate mindfulness, and ultimately restore our connection with ourselves and the world.

So, join us on this enchanting journey as we rediscover the profound and transformative power of nature. Open your heart to the peace it offers, and allow its healing touch to guide you towards a more balanced and fulfilling life.

Sharing the Gift of Nature Meditation

Nature has an incredible power to heal and bring peace to our lives. In our fast-paced, technology-driven world, finding inner peace can sometimes seem like an elusive goal. However, by embracing the gift of nature meditation, we can reconnect with the serenity and tranquility that the natural world offers.

Nature meditation is a practice that involves immersing oneself in the beauty and stillness of the natural environment. It encourages us to engage all our senses and be fully present in the moment. By doing so, we can awaken a sense of awe and wonder that is often forgotten amidst the hustle and bustle of modern life.

One of the first steps in sharing the gift of nature meditation is to find a quiet and peaceful location in nature. It could be a nearby park, a secluded beach, or even a tranquil forest. The key is to choose a place that resonates with you and allows you to feel a deep connection with the natural world.

Once you have found your sacred spot, take a few moments to ground yourself and let go of any distractions or worries. Close your eyes and take a deep breath, allowing the fresh air to fill your lungs. As you exhale, release any tension or stress that you may be holding onto.

Now, open your eyes and begin to observe your surroundings. Notice the vibrant colors, the delicate textures, and the gentle sounds of nature. Allow yourself to be fully present in this moment, embracing the beauty that surrounds you.

As you continue to immerse yourself in nature, start to focus on your breath. Feel the rhythm of your breath as it aligns with the natural world around you. With each inhale, imagine that you are breathing in peace and tranquility. With each exhale, release any negative thoughts or emotions that may be weighing you down.

As you practice nature meditation, remember to be gentle with yourself. It is okay if your mind wanders or if you find it challenging to quiet your thoughts. The goal is not to achieve perfection but rather to embrace the gift of nature and allow it to guide you towards inner peace.

By sharing the gift of nature meditation, we can inspire others to reconnect with the peace that nature provides. Whether it is through guiding friends and loved ones on a nature meditation journey or simply sharing our own experiences, we have the power to help others find solace and serenity in the natural world.

Remember, nature is always there, waiting to offer its healing touch. So, let us come together as a community and share the gift of nature meditation with everyone. By doing so, we can create a world where the peace of nature is cherished and celebrated by all.

Inspiring others to connect with nature's healing touch

In our modern, fast-paced lives, it is easy to become disconnected from the natural world around us. We often find ourselves immersed in the chaos of daily routines, surrounded by concrete walls and artificial lights. However, deep within us, there is a longing to reconnect with the peace and tranquility that nature offers. This subchapter aims to inspire every individual, regardless of age, background, or beliefs, to embrace nature's healing touch and find inner peace in the natural world.

Nature has a unique ability to heal and restore our weary souls. It is a powerful antidote to the stresses and anxieties that plague our minds. When we immerse ourselves in the beauty of nature, we can feel our worries melt away, replaced by a sense of calm and serenity. The gentle rustle of leaves, the soothing sound of flowing water, and the vibrant colors of flowers all work together to awaken our senses and bring us back to our true selves.

Connecting with nature is not limited to grand adventures in far-off places. It can be as simple as taking a walk in a nearby park, tending to a garden, or gazing at the stars on a clear night. The key is to be fully present in the moment, to let go of distractions and immerse ourselves in the beauty and wonder of the natural world. By doing so, we can cultivate a deep sense of peace and reconnect with our inner selves.

But the benefits of nature extend beyond personal well-being. When we connect with nature, we also develop a sense of responsibility and stewardship for the Earth. We become aware of the interconnectedness of all living beings and the importance of preserving and protecting our environment. By inspiring others to connect with nature's healing touch, we can foster a collective consciousness that values and cherishes the natural world.

In conclusion, this subchapter serves as a gentle reminder to everyone, regardless of their background or beliefs, to embrace nature's healing touch and find inner peace in the natural world. Through the simple act of connecting with nature, we can experience a profound transformation within ourselves and develop a deeper understanding of our place in the world. So, take a moment to step outside, breathe in the fresh air, and let nature's healing touch guide you towards inner peace and harmony.

Creating community through nature meditation groups and events

In today's fast-paced and technology-driven world, it is easy to feel disconnected from nature and our inner selves. The constant bombardment of information and the demands of modern life can leave us feeling overwhelmed and disconnected from the peace that nature can bring. However, there is a simple and effective way to reconnect with the natural world and find inner peace – through nature meditation groups and events.

Nature meditation groups and events provide a unique opportunity to come together with like-minded individuals who share a common interest in finding peace and solace in the natural world. These gatherings allow participants to engage in guided meditations and mindfulness practices while surrounded by the beauty of nature. It is a chance to escape the hustle and bustle of everyday life and immerse oneself in the healing power of the Earth.

One of the key benefits of participating in nature meditation groups and events is the sense of community it fosters. When individuals with a shared passion for the peace of nature come together, a sense of belonging and connection is created. The experience of meditating together in nature can be incredibly powerful, as it allows for a deeper connection not only with oneself but also with others and the environment.

These groups and events serve as a safe and supportive space for individuals to explore their inner world and cultivate mindfulness. It is a place where one can let go of stress, worries, and distractions, and instead focus on being present in the moment and fully immersed in the beauty of nature. Through guided meditations and mindful activities, participants can learn to quiet their minds and open their hearts to the peace that nature has to offer.

Nature meditation groups and events can take various forms, from organized hikes and outdoor retreats to regular meetups in local parks or gardens. They can be led by experienced meditation teachers or individuals who simply have a passion for nature and mindfulness. These gatherings can be accessible to people of all ages and backgrounds, making them inclusive and welcoming to everyone.

By participating in nature meditation groups and events, individuals not only find inner peace but also contribute to the creation of a larger community focused on the peace of nature. These gatherings have the potential to inspire and empower individuals to bring mindfulness and environmental consciousness into their daily lives, thereby creating a ripple effect of positive change in the world.

In conclusion, nature meditation groups and events provide a powerful and transformative way to create community and find inner peace. They offer a unique opportunity to connect with like-minded individuals, immerse oneself in the beauty of nature, and cultivate mindfulness. These gatherings are accessible to everyone and have the potential to inspire positive change in individuals and the world at large. So, if you are seeking peace and connection, consider joining a nature meditation group or attending a nature meditation event – you may just find the healing touch of Earth and discover a community that supports your journey towards inner peace.

Empowering individuals to find their inner peace in the natural world

In our fast-paced and technology-driven world, it is easy to feel disconnected from the tranquility and serenity that nature can provide. However, deep within us, there exists an innate connection to the natural world that can bring us immense peace and solace. "Earth's Healing Touch: Mindful Practices for Finding Inner Peace in the Natural World" is a book dedicated to helping individuals harness the power of nature to discover their inner peace and rejuvenate their souls.

This subchapter aims to empower individuals from all walks of life to embrace the peace that nature offers. Whether you are a busy professional seeking respite from the chaos of daily life or a nature enthusiast yearning to deepen your connection with the environment, this chapter will guide you through transformative practices that will lead you to find your inner peace in the natural world.

Nature has a remarkable ability to restore balance and harmony within us. By immersing ourselves in its beauty, we can tap into an endless source of serenity and clarity. This subchapter explores various techniques and mindful practices that can help you embrace the peace of nature.

From meditative walks in the forest to cultivating a garden, this chapter offers a range of activities that can be incorporated into your daily routine. It emphasizes the importance of mindfulness and being fully present in the moment as you engage with nature. Whether it is observing the delicate petals of a flower or listening to the rhythmic sound of crashing waves, these practices encourage a deeper connection with the natural world.

Moreover, this subchapter delves into the healing power of nature and its ability to nurture our mental and emotional well-being. It explores the concept of ecotherapy and how spending time in nature can alleviate stress, anxiety, and depression. Through engaging anecdotes and scientific research, readers will gain a comprehensive understanding of the positive impact that immersing oneself in nature can have on their overall well-being.

"Earth's Healing Touch: Mindful Practices for Finding Inner Peace in the Natural World" is a guidebook for individuals seeking to restore their sense of inner peace and find solace in the beauty of the natural world. By embracing the practices outlined in this subchapter, readers will embark on a transformative journey towards a more peaceful and harmonious existence, ultimately leading to a deeper connection with themselves and the environment around them.

Conclusion: Cultivating Inner Peace through Nature Meditation

In our fast-paced and technologically-driven world, finding inner peace has become an increasingly elusive goal for many individuals. The constant noise, distractions, and stressors of modern life can leave us feeling overwhelmed and disconnected from ourselves and the natural world around us. However, there is a powerful and accessible solution that has been available to us all along – cultivating inner peace through nature meditation.

Throughout this book, we have explored the profound healing and rejuvenating power of connecting with nature. We have learned how spending time in natural environments can reduce stress, enhance mental clarity, and promote overall well-being. By immersing ourselves in the beauty and tranquility of the natural world, we can find solace and restore balance to our lives.

Nature meditation, as we have discovered, is a practice that involves intentionally focusing our attention on the sights, sounds, and sensations of the natural world. It is a way to quiet the mind, open the heart, and cultivate a deep sense of inner peace. Through this practice, we can develop a greater appreciation for the beauty and interconnectedness of all living things.

The benefits of nature meditation extend beyond the individual. As we connect with nature on a deeper level, we become more aware of our role as stewards of the Earth. We recognize the importance of preserving and protecting our natural environments for future generations to enjoy. By fostering a sense of peace within ourselves, we are also contributing to the collective peace of our planet.

So, how can each one of us cultivate inner peace through nature meditation? It starts with making a conscious commitment to prioritize time spent in nature. Whether it is a daily walk in the park, a weekend hike, or simply sitting under a tree in our backyard, every moment spent connecting with nature is a step towards finding inner peace.

Additionally, incorporating mindfulness into our nature experiences can deepen our connection and bring greater awareness to our surroundings. By focusing on our breath, grounding ourselves in the present moment, and fully immersing ourselves in the sensory experience of nature, we can quiet our minds and nourish our souls.

In conclusion, cultivating inner peace through nature meditation is a journey that is available to everyone. By taking the time to connect with the natural world, we can find solace, restore balance, and experience a profound sense of well-being. Let us embrace the healing touch of the Earth and allow nature to guide us towards a more peaceful and harmonious existence.

Milton Keynes UK
Ingram Content Group UK Ltd.
UKHW020238221123
432980UK00016B/1189